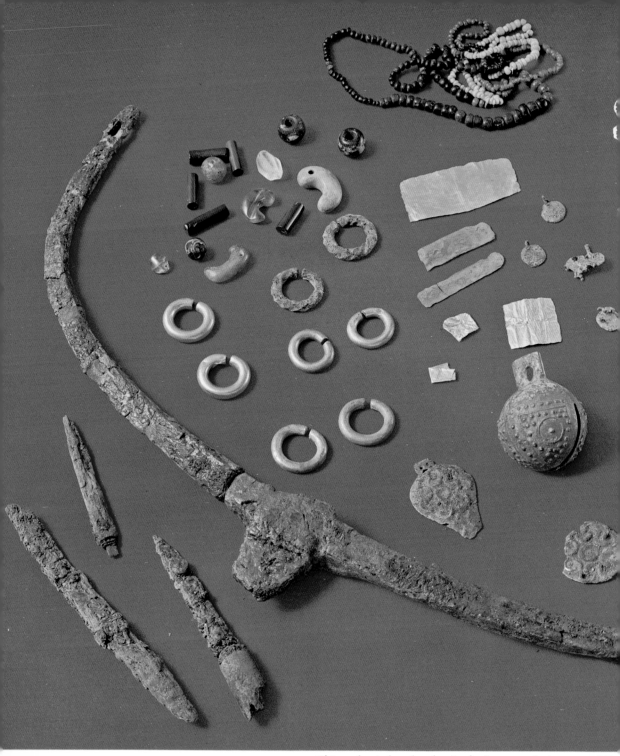

Objects buried under the Asukadera pagoda (see page 98)

GUIDE TO THE
ASUKA HISTORICAL MUSEUM
NARA NATIONAL
CULTURAL PROPERTIES
RESEARCH INSTITUTE,
NARA, JAPAN

Compiled by
ASUKA HISTORICAL MUSEUM

English translation by
WILLIAM R. CARTER

Edition/Asuka Historical Museum
Printer/Kansai Prsess Lim.
First Printing of English Edition, 1978

FOREWORD

Asuka, some 1300 and more years ago, was home to Japan's ruling dynasty and was thus, for more than a century, the capital of the country. It was at this time that our country adopted much of the relatively matured culture and administrative methodology of China and the Korean peninsula, and it was here that a unified national state was for the first time established in Japan.

It was here that Buddhism was introduced and Buddhist art saw its first flower. New types of knowledge and new working techniques were introduced one after another, and Asuka progressively consolidated its functions as the administrative and cultural center of the time. Even today, the palace and temple sites, *kofun* (tumulus graves), stone figures and other man-made reminders of the times are left behind in considerable number. Moreover, one may here appreciate retrospectfully, wistfully perhaps, the natural features and other places written about or associated with a great many of the famous poems in the *Man'yōshū*.

The Asuka Historical Museum was established in order to help visitors gain a better understanding both of the historical significance of the Asuka region and also of the various material expressions of its earlier culture which have been handed down to us. In addition to the museum exhibit itself, there is also a historical materials reading room.

Excavation studies in Asuka are being continued, and it is our intention to supplement the exhibit as the results of these studies become known in the future.

We should like here to express our profound thanks to all the many persons who gave their kind cooperation in the making of this exhibit and guidebook.

Asuka Historical Museum

CONTENTS

ASUKA PREHISTORY AND ORIGINS OF THE HISTORICAL PERIOD

From the Stone Age to Beginning
of the "Asuka Period"

a b
c d f
e g
h

The Asuka of 3000 Years Ago (*Jōmon* Period)

At this time the Asuka region was covered by woodlands and moors, scene of the swift rounds of deer and wild boar. Humans were already settled in scattered locations. They made use of earthen vessels and stone tools, and lived by hunting wild animals and collecting fruits and berries.

The Asuka of 2000 Years Ago (*Yayoi* Period)

There were at this time in Asuka wet rice fields, and agricultural villages had come into being. With the course of time, iron blades were making their appearance, replacing implements of stone. Among the people, distinctions were beginning to be made between those who exercised control and those who were controlled.

The Asuka of 1600 Years Ago (Tumulus Period)

In the Japanese islands of this time, members of the ruling house and of other powerful clans were vigorously pushing forward the unification of the country. As one means of displaying their power they built for themselves large tumulus graves (*kofun*), heaped over with high mounds of earth. Asuka at this time had not yet attained its later distinction as the country's administrative center, and tumulus graves were not yet being built here. It is worth noting that at this time, or soon thereafter, newcomers arriving from the Korean peninsula were beginning to settle throughout the area of present-day Asuka Village (Asuka-mura) and in other nearby localities.

The Asuka of 1400 Years Ago (Beginning of the "Asuka Period")

Together with the acquisition of power and influence by the Soga clan, a wealthy family which exercised some degree of control over the immigrant settlers in the region, Asuka rapidly became the pivot of politics and culture. The newly arrived Buddhist culture saw here its first bloom. Temples, imperial residences and the homes of other wealthy and influential families were built in close proximity to one another, and the Japanese nation-state of ancient times, with Asuka at its center, proceeded to take form.

a, b	Jomon earthenware	l earth digging tool	
c, d, e	Yayoi earthenware	m stone spear	r iron arrowhead
f	Sue ware (Tumulus Period)	n stone arrowheads	s magatama ("curved jewel,"
g, h	Haji ware (Tumulus Period)	o ishibōchō (stone blade used	probably having symbolic
i clay figure		for reaping)	meaning)
j knife		p single-bladed axe	t bronze arrowhead
k stone arrowheads		q large ishibōchō	u spindle

2   Jōmon Period   Yayoi Period   Tumulus P

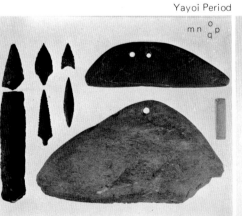

→ *Asuka Daibutsu (Asukadera)*

SCOPE OF THE "ASUKA PERIOD"

As a periodization term, "Asuka Period" was first used around the year 1900 in reference to architectural and art history, and had as its original proponents Sekino Tadashi and Okakura Tenshin. Sekino designated the "Asuka Period" as that era most strongly influenced by Korean art, extending, in his estimation, from the reign of Empress Suiko (592~628) up to the time of the Taika Reform (645). Okakura considered the "Asuka Period" to extend, in its broadest sense, from the introduction of Buddhism — he favored choice of the date 552 — up to the transfer of the capital to Heijō (Nara) in 710, during most of which time the dynastic residence was to be found in one or another part of the Asuka region. However, for purposes of an "exact year demarcation," he limited the period to the interval between the introduction of Buddhism and the beginning of the reign of Emperor Tenji (667). Sekino conceived of the "Asuka Period" as that period leading up to what he termed the "Nara Period" (i.e., Hakuhō and Tempyō Periods) characterized by influences from Táng China, while Okakura similarly conceived of the "Asuka Period," in his narrower sense, as preceding what he termed the "Tempyō Period" (beginning in 667).

According to present usage, "Asuka Period," when referring broadly to Japanese history as a whole, designates the time from around the reign of Empress Suiko up to the transfer of the capital to Heijō, in approximation of the broader sense of the term as used by Okakura. However, since use of the term by itself is in many cases liable to imprecision, it is more common to employ such terms as "the first half of the 7th century" or the name of a specific emperor or empress.

In the specific fields of art history, architecture and archaeology, however, the term "Asuka Period" is still commonly employed in the more narrow sense used by Sekino.

3

"ASUKA" AS A PLACE NAME

Today the term "Asuka" commonly refers to a broad area centering around present-day Asuka-mura, but including parts of Kashihara-shi, Sakurai-shi, Takatori-chō, etc. However, in the 7th and 8th centuries, "Asuka" was used primarily in reference to the area bounded on the west by the Asuka River, bounded on the north by Mount Kagu (*Kaguyama*), and having its southern boundary in the vicinity of the Tachibanadera. The more northerly area of the Fujiwara capital and also the present-day districts of Toyura, Hinokuma, etc. (within Asuka-mura) seem not at that time to have been included in the designation "Asuka." In this museum, however, we employ "Asuka" in the first-mentioned, broader sense of the term.

In old documents, "Asuka" may be found written in various ways, with differing sets of Chinese characters. There is no single generally accepted explanation for the origin of writing "Asuka" with the two characters meaning, respectively, "to fly" and "bird." One hypothesis is that it derives from the stock epithet "of flying birds" (*tobu tori no*) commonly prefixed to the place name "Asuka" in poetry. Another theory has it that these two characters were first applied as the result of the recorded appearance of what was alleged to be a particularly auspicious bird (*shuchō*) in the year 685 (15th year of Emperor Tenmu's reign). Other writings of the same place name use combinations of either two or three characters whose phonetic values render, in apposition, the sequence *asu-ka*, or *a-su-ka*. (See Japanese text for examples.)

FROM THE AGE OF NEAR-AUTONOMOUS GŌZOKU TO THE AGE OF RITSURYŌ CONTROLS

After the 4th and 5th centuries, the moving forces behind the country's politics at the "center" were a number of powerful and near-autonomous wealthy families (*gōzoku*), of which the most important, at least for ceremonial purposes, was the house of the ruling emperor. Around the middle of the 6th century, effective power was largely in the grip of two clans, the Mononobe and the Soga, but after 587, when the Mononobe were purged from their position of shared oligarchy about the dynastic house, administration tended to be monopolized by the Soga, and at the same time the Asuka region emerged more and more unequivocally as the country's administrative and cultural center.

Conditions in China came to be better known through the medium of envoys to the Suí and Táng capitals, and as Suí and Táng power began to extend into Korea, there appeared in Japan new movements which were opposed to this and other international and domestic trends, and which aimed at throwing off old structures and building a stronger and more durable Japanese state.

In 645 (first year of the Taika Reform), the Soga clan was brought down from its position of power by a coalition led by Nakatomi-no-Kamatari and Prince Naka-no-Ōe, thus heralding the end of an age of domination by near-autonomous *gōzoku*. Prince Naka-no-Ōe (who later became Emperor Tenji, reigning 668–671) and his associates, while on the one hand pursuing armed struggles on the Korean peninsula against Táng and Silla (southeastern Korean) forces, sought on the other hand to build a new state which would make use of administrative systems adopted from China. The latter task was for the most part completed during the reigns of Tenmu (672–686) and his wife Jitō (686–697).

The Chinese-inspired *ritsuryō* system of penal and administrative law was established as the country's fundamental legal code, and the general body of the populace, which had throughout the country lived under domination by near-autonomous *gōzoku*, became subject to the control of the central administration, through the intermediary of offices for that purpose established in the capital region and in the outlying provinces. The Fujiwara capital (*Fujiwara-kyō*), completed for occupancy in 694 (the 8th year of Empress Jitō's reign), may be said to have been at the same time intended as a sort of monument to commemorate what was thought of as the completion (nominally, at least) of a nation-state operating under the new regulations of the *ritsuryō* system.

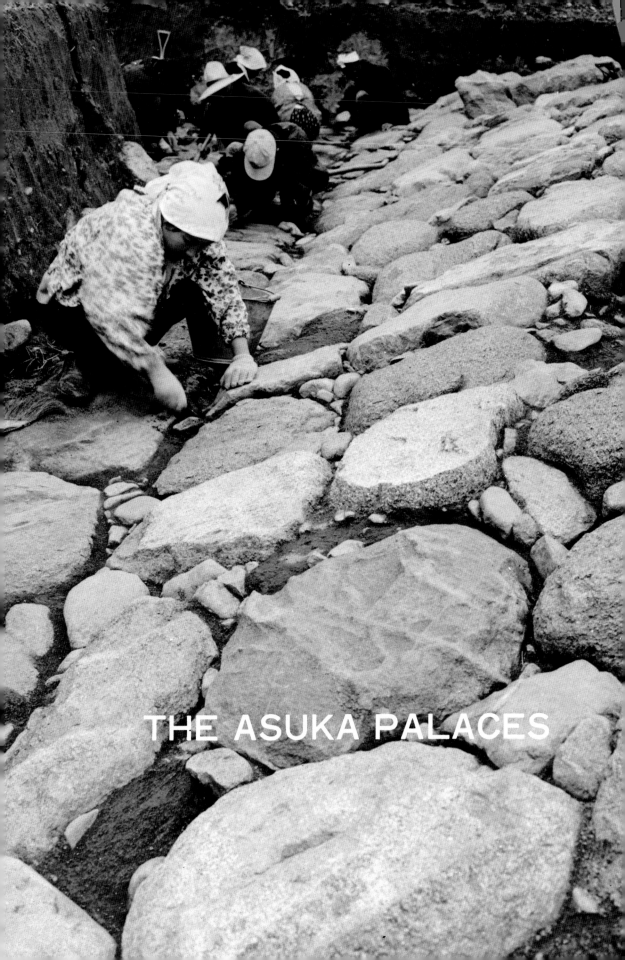

THE ASUKA PALACES

THE ASUKA PALACES

If we accept the recorded tradition, it would appear that already as early as the 4th and 5th centuries Emperors Ōjin and Ingyō had residences in the Asuka region. In the earlier half of the 6th century, residences of Emperors Kenzō and Senka were built here, but it was not until after the building of Empress Suiko's Toyura-no-miya at the end of the 6th century that imperial residences came to be built in the Asuka region in fairly regular sequence. While these "palaces" (*miya*, a word also used to designate buildings or shrines of a ritual significance) were from the first built to serve chiefly as residences for one or another ruler, they also had the function of providing a place for the exercise of certain political, administrative and ceremonial activities. Palaces were moved with each change of emperor, and sometimes were moved two or three times during one and the same reign.

As the framework of the nation-state began to assume a more ordered form, palace construction came to include, in imitation of the Chinese practice, a large number of administrative offices in addition to the emperor's residence itself. Finally, there came to be built up around the palace an urbanized zone (*kyō*) subdivided by streets.

6

Asuka breezes that once curled back the palace maidens' sleeves
Seeing now the court so far, they blow quite purposelessly

Man'yōshū 51

(composed by Prince Shiki
after the capital was moved to Fujiwara-no-miya)

↑ *Excavation of the Fujiwara palace (1934). The clump of trees at the top marks the raised earth foundation on the site of the imperial council hall (see page 4).*

← *Stone-paved drainage ditch at the supposed site of the Asuka Kiyomihara palace.*

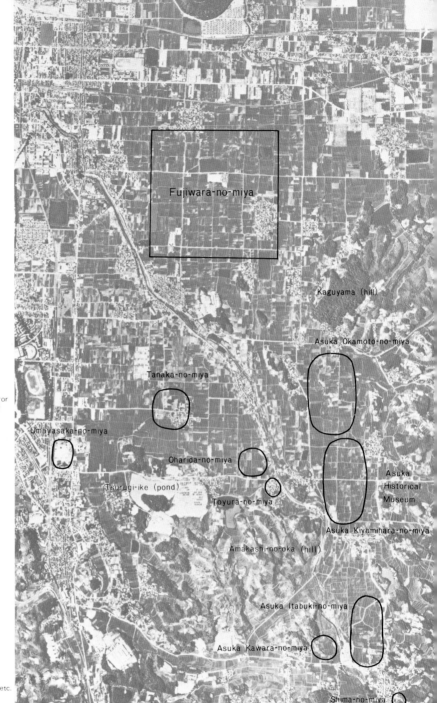

Miminashiyama (hill)

Fujiwara-no-miya

Kaguyama (hill)

Asuka Okamoto-no-miya

Tanaka-no-miya

Umayasaka-no-miya

Oharida-no-miya

Asuka Historical Museum

Tsurugi-ike (pond)

Toyura-no-miya

Asuka Kiyomihara-no-miya

Amakashi-no-oka (hill)

Asuka Itabuki-no-miya

Asuka Kawara-no-miya

Shima-no-miya

PLACES OF THE ASUKA PERIOD

Palace Name	Beginning of Occupancy	Resident Emperor or Empress (+)
Toyura-no-miya	592	Suiko (+)
Oharida-no-miya	603	Suiko (+)
Asuka Okamoto-no-miya	630	Jomei
Tanaka-no-miya	636	Jomei
Umayasaka-no-miya	640	Jomei
Kudara-no-miya (outside Asuka, in present-day Nara-ken, Kōryō-chō)	640	Jomei
Asuka Itabuki-no miya	643	Kōgyoku (+)
Naniwa Nagara Toyosaki-no-miya (outside Asuka in present-day Ōsaka-shi)	645	Kōtoku
Asuka Itabuki-no-miya	655	Saimei (+) (same person as Kōgyoku)
Asuka Kawara-no-miya	655	Saimei (+)
Nochi no Asuka Okamoto-no-miya	656	Saimei (+)
Asakura no Tachibana no Hironiwa-no-miya (outside Asuka in present-day Fukuoka-ken)	661	Saimei (+)
Ōmi Ōtsu-no-miya (outside Asuka, in present-day Shiga-ken, Ōtsu-shi)	667	Tenji
Shima-no-miya	672	Tenmu
Asuka Okamoto-no-miya	672	Tenmu
Asuka Kiyomihara no-miya	672	Tenmu
Fujiwara-no-miya	694	Jitō (+) Monmu Genmei (+)
Nara-no-miya (outside Asuka, in present day Nara-shi)	710	Genmei (+), etc.

Having left behind the old home in Asuka of flying birds
Must the surroundings of my lord no longer be in view?

Man'yōshū 78

(composed by Empress Genmei in the
spring of 710, stopping her palanquin
during the move to Nara-no-miya)

PALACE COLUMNS (*Miyabashira*)

The stately appearance of Asuka's imperial residences is celebrated in the phrase *miyabashira futoshiki imashi* ("palace columns stoutly set"), found in the *Man'yōshū*. Most of the structures in a given palace were of a *hottate-bashira* type construction, with the lower ends of the thick supporting posts set into the ground. Structures of a Chinese type with supporting posts resting atop foundation stones at approximately ground level were, even in the case of the Fujiwara and Nara palaces, only partially employed. As seen, for example, in the "poem composed by a workman engaged in the building of the Fujiwara palace" *(Man'yōshū* No. 50), most of the timber used for the supporting posts of the imperial palaces was cut from mountains in Ōmi (present-day Shiga-ken), then tied together on rafts and transported over considerable distances to the capital.

⬇ *Hottate-bashira at the supposed site of Itabuki-no-miya.*

a Sen with lotus design.
b Earthenware from Oharida-no-miya site.
c Gilt bronze pot from Oharida-no-miya site.

Man'yōshū No. 50

Composed by one of the workmen engaged
in the building of the Fujiwara palace

Our sovereign who rules in peace
Child of a high and shining sun
To govern the land at her command
Conceived in godlike fashion
To bring into lofty being
A palace at Fujiwara, whose name
Reminds us of rough woven fiber.
Besides both earth and heaven
Are drawn together in this intent.
Into Yasoujigawa of warrior fame
We have sent floating like seaweed
Bundles of cypress logs fit for lumber
From sleeve-like Tanakamiyama
In Ōmi-no-kuni of stone-running streams.
Taking these up, the boisterous folk,
Forgetting their homes and thinking
Not the least bit about themselves
Like wild ducks are buoyed in the water.
To the sun-palace that we build
May the missions of lands unknown
Come over and across by Kose road
And may our own land last forever.
Even those wondrous tortoises
That bear diagrams on their shells
Tell of a new age arising.
And watching how one busily toils
Fixing the bundles of transported timber
Into the numerous rafts
To be brought upstream by Izumi's rivers
It must seem indeed of godlike motivation.

8

OHARIDA-NO-MIYA (603~628)

This palace was occupied by Empress Suiko for a quarter-century. When Ono-no-Imoko, emissary to Suí China, returned to Japan bringing with him the Suí envoy Péi Shìqìng, it was here that the Chinese envoy presented his letters of accreditation. The site of the Oharida palace is thought to be in the northern part of the present-day Toyura district (*ōaza*) of Asuka-mura, in the neighborhood (*koaza*) known as Furumiya. In the Meiji period a gilt bronze pot with four handlerings was unearthed here from beside a platform of raised earth. Excavation studies have revealed the remains of buildings, drainage ditches and courtyards to the south of this platform, and also such artifacts as *sen* (a type of brick) with lotus designs. ⬆ *Remains of Oharida-no-miya courtyard. A tree is seen standing in the center of the raised earth platform mentioned in the text.*

9

c

ASUKA ITABUKI-NO-MIYA (643~645, also occupied in 655)

It was here that Soga-no-Iruka was assassinated in 645 (the 4th year of Empress Kôgyoku's reign). The roof of the palace was presumably shingled with wooden boards (*itabuki*) in contradistinction to former palaces, whose roofs are believed to have been for the most part thatched. The buildings were lost to fire in 655 (first year of Kôgyoku's second reign, in which she is known to history as Saimei). The remains of stone pavements, buildings, and a large well have been excavated in the Oka district of Asuka-mura, in a place which tradition had long held to be an abandoned palace site. Although this site is provisionally designated as that of the Asuka Itabuki-no-miya, some scholars hold the view that it might be rather the site of the Shima-no-miya or the Asuka Kiyomihara-no-miya. ↑ *Stone pavement around large well at supposed site of* → *Asuka Itabuki-no-miya.*

ASUKA KAWARA-NO-MIYA (655~656)

It was here that Empress Saimei transferred her residence in the winter of 655, in the wake of the fire which had destroyed the Asuka Itabuki-no-miya, where she had assumed rulership (for the second time) earlier the same year. When excavation studies were made at the Kawaradera, it was discovered that there were drainage ditches predating the construction of the temple, and among the artifacts unearthed therefrom were a comb, a *geta* (wooden clog), and clay utensils. These drainage ditches are thought to be part of the construction of the Asuka Kawara-no-miya. Further discovery brought to light the stone receptacles (*kara-ishiki*) which housed the bottom ends of the pivot-and-hole type shafts that formed part of the structure of the palace doors.

10

a Clay utensil found at the supposed site of Asuka Itabuki-no-miya.
b Clay utensils found at the site of Asuka Kawara-no-miya.

a

b

Alignment of wooden supporting posts in what was a roofed passageway at supposed site of Asuka Itabuki-no-miya.

Drainage ditch where wooden clog was found at site of Asuka Kawara-no-miya.

Kara-ishiki of the Kawara-no-miya ⬇

A *kara-ishiki* is a stone used as a receptacle for a door shaft. In contrast to the *kara-ishiki* used in the foundation-stone type construction of the Kawaradera, the *kara-ishiki* of the Kawara-no-miya, in addition to having cavities hollowed into the stones themselves, were designed to have affixed to their sides deep-set *hottate-bashira* (see page 8), from which fact we may surmise that the doors were part of a *hottate-bashira* type building.

d Wooden clog, Kawara-no-miya.

11

d

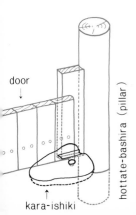

door

hottate-bashira (pillar)

kara-ishiki

ASUKA KIYOMIHARA-NO-MIYA (672~694)

It was here that Emperor Tenmu, who as Prince Ōama had defeated Prince Ōtomo (son of his elder brother, Emperor Tenji) in the Jinshin Disturbance of 672, assumed the throne upon moving the capital back to Asuka from Ōmi (on the shore of Lake Biwa, present-day Shiga-ken). It was also here that his wife and successor, Empress Jitō, completed the legal code known as the Asuka Kiyomihara-ryō.

As befit an era which saw a strengthening of the foundations of the legally administered *ritsuryō* nation-state, the Asuka Kiyomihara-no-miya boasted several *chōdō* (administrative head quarters for the various ministries), a *daianden*, and a *daigokuden* (imperial council hall). Around the palace an urban zone (*kyō*) began to develop, and a government office, the *kyōshiki*, was established to regulate its affairs. The palace is thought to have been located in the vicinity of the present-day Asuka Primary School, within the grounds of which there are vestiges of ancient stone pavements. To the south of the school, excavations have revealed the remains of buildings and a stone-paved drainage ditch laid in a square approximately 22.5 meters per side. ➡ *Square stone-paved ditch near supposed site of Asuka Kiyomihara-no-miya.*

SUPPOSED SITE OF THE SHIMA-NO-MIYA

The Shima-no-miya is mentioned in historical literature as having originally been a residence of Soga-no-Umako, later made into an imperial palace occupied for many years by Prince Kusakabe (son of Emperor Tenmu). A handsome pond, with a stone-paved floor, has been excavated in the district of Asuka-mura which bears the name Shimanoshō.

Poems by Shima palace attendants after Prince Kusakabe's death

I serve at my post
By the eastern cascade gate
But neither yesterday nor today
Was any word of summons sent

Man'yōshū 184

At the Shima court
Lit by the morning sun
Dismally no human sound is heard
How sad to the very core

Man'yōshū ▮

a Remains of pond on supposed site of Shima-no-miya

12

Our great king, a god indeed, has made into a model city
Those swampy fields where chestnut ponies trudged
In mud up to their bellies   *Man'yōshū 4260*

Our great king, god that he is, has turned into his capital
A marsh where waterfowl used to mingle

Man'yōshū 4261

(composed after the end of the
Jinshin Disturbance in 672 and the
establishment of the capital at
Asuka Kiyomihara-no-miya)

b Clay utensils from site of Asuka Kiyomihara-no-miya.

b

14

FUJIWARA-NO-MIYA (694~710)

Special Historical Site

The Fujiwara-no-miya was a full-fledged Chinese-style palace constructed by Empress Jitō as the capital of Japan's *ritsuryō*-administered nation-state. Centered on the present-day Takadono district of Kashihara-shi and surrounded on three sides by the "three Yamato mountains," the palace covered an area of approximately one kilometer per side. In the center was the *dairi* (sovereign's residential quarters) and the *chōdōin*, an area with ministerial offices arrayed on either side of a central courtyard used for ceremonial activities. The outer perimeter of the palace was ringed with a tall wooden fence and a moat. On the present site of the former *daigokuden* (main audience hall, the most important building within the *chōdōin*), vestiges of an elevated platform, in local parlance known as the "*ōmiya dodan*" ("earth platform of the great palace"), rise above the surrounding rice fields.

⬆ *The ōmiya dodan as seen from the site of the south gate.*

🔽 *Remains of government offices.*

➡ *Aerial view of Fujiwara-no-miya site.*

a   Reconstruction of part of Fujiwara-no-miya roof, using original tiles.

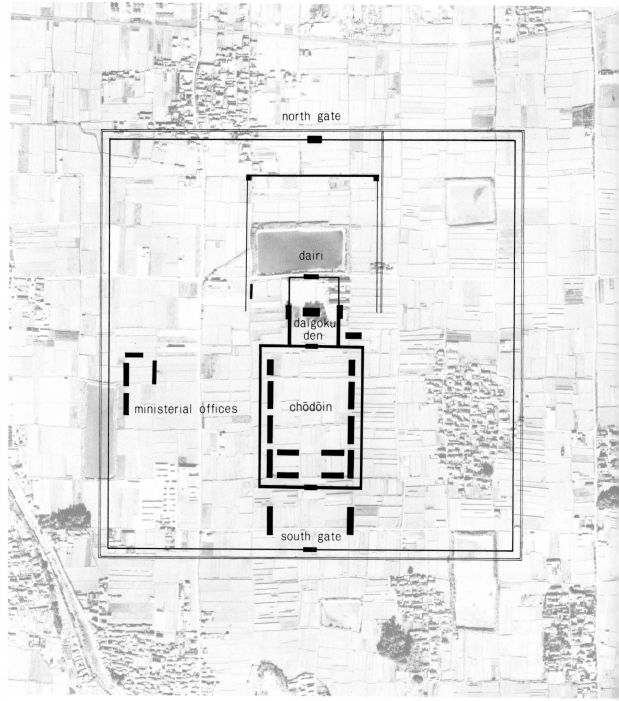

north gate

dairi

daigoku den

ministerial offices

chōdōin

south gate

15

THE FUJIWARA CAPITAL CITY

As well befit the head city of the *ritsuryō* nation-state, Fujiwara-kyō was patterned after the Chinese capitals. Here, for the first time in Japan, city streets were constructed in a checkerboard arrangement. The exact area of the capital city is not known, but it is thought to have extended approximately 2 kilometers from east to west and 3 kilometers from north to south, bounded on the east, west and north, respectively, by the Nakatsumichi, Shimotsumichi, and Yoko-ōji, all three of which were important trunk roads of the time. The custom of calling the eastern half of the capital the "left capital" *(sakyō)* and the western half the "right capital" *(ukyō)* was in Japan first practiced at Fujiwara-kyō. City blocks, delineated by streets *(ōji)*, seem, in contrast to Nara-kyō (Nara) and Heian-kyo (Kyoto), not to have been designated by numerical combinations of *jō* (north-south subdivisions) and *bō* (east-west subdivisions), but rather by proper names such as Ohari-machi or Hayashi-machi.

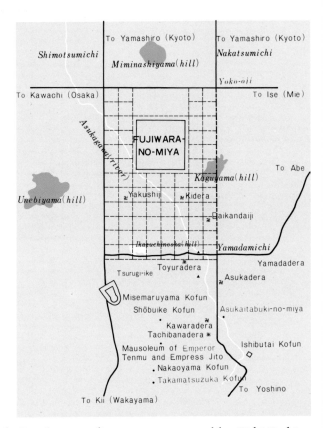

Map showing Fujiwara-kyō and surroundings, as reconstructed by Kishi Toshio.

16

a   Clay utensils from Fujiwara-kyō.   b   Unfinished plow from site of Fujiwara-kyō.

a

HOUSEHOLD REGISTERS

Under the *ritsuryō* legal system, household registers *(koseki)* listing each person in the country were compiled to serve as the basis for levying taxes and conscripting soldiers. During the period of the Fujiwara capital when the *ritsuryō* system was being perfected, the principle was established of compiling household registers once every six years.

➤ Part of a household register from Chikuzen-no-kuni (present-day Fukuoka-ken) dating from the year 702. This is the oldest extant household register in Japan and is said to have been formerly housed in the Shōsōin.

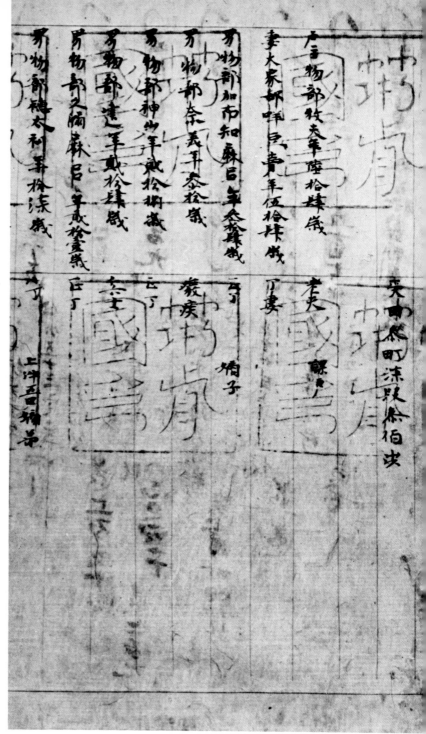

17

WOODEN TABLETS

As the *ritsuyō* legal system took shape, it became more and more common for government offices to use written records in the handling of administrative affairs. These written records took the form of wooden tablets *(mokkan)* bearing ink-written Chinese characters such as those which have been discovered at the site of Fujiwara-no-miya and the supposed site of *Asuka Itabuki-no-miya*. The *mokkan* were of several types, including documents, labels for goods in transport, and tallies for other classification purposes. They provide important new materials for learning about the culture, finances, organization of government offices and overall administrative system of the time. For example, while it had been known that Japan in the Nara Period was divided into sixty-odd units known as *kuni* and each of these *kuni* was divided into several *kōri*, it had not been known when the Chinese character that, during the Nara period, was used to represent *kōri*, first came into use. Through an examination of recently excavated *mokkan*, it has been established that previous to the Taihō legal code (702), the word *kōri* was written with a different character.

「己亥年十月上挾国阿波評松里」　　「商陸漆斤」

「受被給薬　車前子一升　西辛一両
　　　　　久参四両　右三種　　」
（obverse）

「多治麻内親王宮政人正八位下陽胡甥」
（reverse）

Two illustrations on left: Reverse and obverse of the same *mokkan*. This tally was a communication by which one Yako-no-Oi, an immigrant official in the service of Princess Tajima (daughter of Emperor Tenmu), made a requisition for various quantities of three medicinal plants including *ōbako* fruit (a kind of plantain), used as a diuretic and cough medicine.

Right (above): Label attached to taxes in kind collected in 699 from Kazusa-no-kuni, Awa-no-kōri (later Awa-no-kuni, in southern part of present-day Chiba-ken).

Right (below): Label attached to 7 *kin* (about 4.5 kilograms) of *shōriku* (a medicinal herb used as a diuretic).

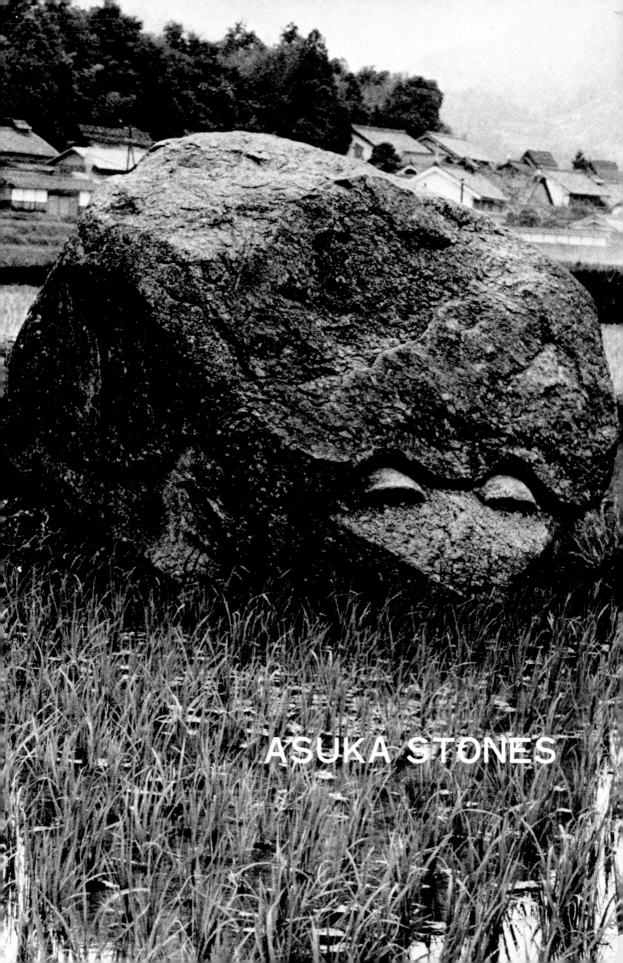

ASUKA STONES

ASUKA STONES

In various parts of the Asuka region are to be found unusually shaped granite stones and st
carved figures. Apart from the *Shumisen-seki* (a garden fixture carved to suggest Mount Sumēr
Buddhist mythology) or the male-female stone carving which likewise was designed as a foun
the purposes originally associated with the other worked stones, bearing such names as *Masud
iwafune, Sakafune-ishi, Kame-ishi, Miroku-ishi, Nimen-seki*, etc., have been for the most part
gotten. The male-female stone carving, the *Nimen-seki*, the *Saru-ishi* ("monkey stones"), etc.
different from the *haniwa* and other stone human figures made during the former Kofun (Tu
lus) Period. Brimming with a droll sort of sturdiness, they display what is also a completely di
ent quality from that of the later Buddhist sculptures.

⬆ *Four Saru-ishi at the grave of Kibi-hime* Ō, *seen from the north.*
⬅ *Kame-ishi ("tortoise stone")*

MALE-FEMALE STONE CARVING

Height 1.7 meters   7th century
Unearthed at Asuka-mura, Ishigami

This stone carving was used as a fountain in an Asuka Period garden. It was designed so that water could rise through a hole at the bottom and discharge from both the mouth of the female and from a stemmed drinking cup held up to the mouth of the male. Today the lower part of the cup is missing and one sees the branched cavity through which water once flowed. The facial characteristics attract notice for their exotic cast. The carving was unearthed in 1903 from the neighborhood known as Ishigami, 600 meters to the southwest of the present museum. Since the 1930's, it has also been familiarly referred to by the term *dōsojin* (a name also applied to phallic-shaped stones associated with folk religion and certain Shinto shrines).

21

Photometric sketch indicating exact dimensions of the male-female stone carving
(Square sections mark 20 cm. units.)

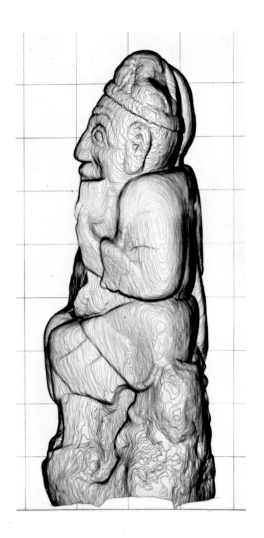

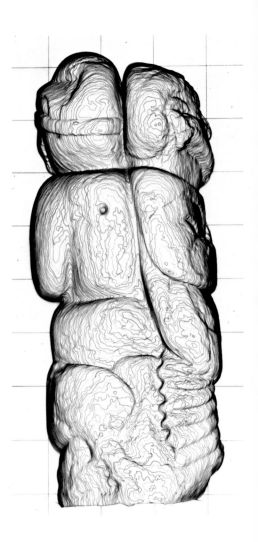

22

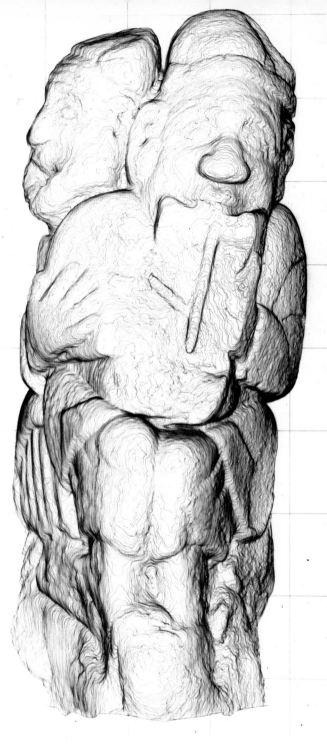

23

SHUMISEN-SEKI

Height 2.3 meters   7th century
Unearthed at Asuka-mura, Ishigami

This stone, together with the anthropomorphic stone carving exhibited in the museum lobby, was unearthed at Ishigami in the Meiji period. It is called the *Shumisen-seki* ("Mount Sumêru stone") because of its overall shape and also the mountain patterns carved in relief on part of its outer surface. It was a garden accessory used as a fountain, and a drainage trench and stone pavements have been found in the same vicinity. The *Shumisen* (Japanese pronunciation of the Mount Sumêru of Buddhist mythology) mentioned in historical records as having been built to the west of the Asukadera and in the Kawara district to the east of Amakashi-no-oka in connection with entertainments provided for *Emishi* (an ethnic group possibly related to the Ainu) and persons of "southern" origin in the reign of the Empress Saimei (655~661) were probably something of this kind.

➡ *Shumisen-seki and chart showing its construction.*

Structure of the Shumisen-seki

Each of the three stones has an inner cavity. Water was drawn up through the bottom, stored inside the lower stone, and made to spurt out on four sides from miniature holes.

The center stone is not directly connected with the lower one, and it appears that there was originally another stone between them. Also, from the structure of the bottom surface of the lowers stone, we can surmise that it originally had another stone beneath it.

a   Inner surface of lower stone.   b   Water spurting from small hole.
c   Mountain ridge carved in relief on support for halo behind the Kudara Kannon (Hōryūji).
d   "Ocean and seashore mirror" among treasures donated to Imperial household by the Hōryūji.
    (Now housed in the Tokyo National Museum.)

24

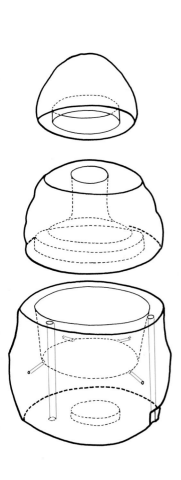

NIMEN-SEKI ("two-faced stone") 7th century

This stone is today found within the precincts of the Tachibanadera, but it was brought here from a nearby area after the beginning of the Edo Period. According to certain present-day interpretations, its two faces are taken to represent good and evil. Its back side is flattened, a fact suggesting that it may originally have been used in conjunction with another stone.

a Jinmen-seki   b Saru-ishi at Takatori Castle site   c – e Saru-ishi at Kibihime-Ō grave

SARU-ISHI

Heights: 95, 90, 87, 115 centimeters
7th century   Asuka-mura, Hirata

Four of these figures stand on the plot of ground designated as the grave of Kibi-hime Ō. They are called *saru-ishi* ("monkey stones") because of their queer shapes. Three of the figures have faces on the back side as well as the front. It seems possible that the account in the 12th century *Konjaku monogatari* about "stones of demonic form" on the embankment of an emperor's mausoleum to the south of the Karudera may refer to these stones. The Presently known Saru-ishi, five in all, were excavated from a field to the south of Emperor Kinmei's mausoleum during the Edo (Tokugawa) Period and moved to their present locations. One of them is now on the site of the ruins of Takatori Castle, some 5 kilometers to the southeast of the Kibihime-Ō grave.

ont and back, respectively, of the second
ru-ishi from the north, Kibihime-Ō grave.

SAKAFUNE-ISHI

Length 5.3 meters
7th century   Asuka-mura, Asuka-ōaza

The upper surface has circular and oval indentations connected by narrow channels. In the Edo Period, it was called "the *sake* trough of an old-time chieftain." It is indeed thought by some to have been a sort of trough for squeezing the moisture out of *sake* lees, while it is thought by others to have been used in the preparation of oil or medicine. However, there is also a theory that the stone was related to some sort of garden fixture. In any case it appears that water was carried to the stone by stone conduits and clay pipes, remains of which have been discovered at a somewhat higher elevation 40 meters to the east. Some 400 meters to the southwest, on the east bank of the Asuka River, researchers excavated two stones which, as a set, were designed to channel the flow of water. In imitation of the name given the above-mentioned stone, these are also called *sakafune-ishi*. They are presently in Kyoto.   ⬆*Sakafune-ishi*

STONES WITH PATTERNED RELIEF CARVINGS

7th century   Asuka-mura, Toyura

In the Toyura district, there are four stones with relief carvings similar to those on the *Shumisen-seki*. One of these is on the grounds of the Kōgenji, and the others were used as part of the construction of a tunnel built in the Edo Period to bring water to the Wada Pond.

a Two stones, also called Sakafune-ishi, found beside the Asukagawa (river)

b Pattern on stone at Kōgenji   c Pattern on stone from Wada Pond tunnel

28

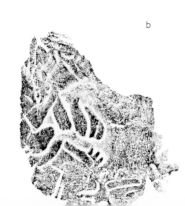

Masuda no Iwafune as it appears today, and a 1791 sketch from Yamato meishozue. ⬆ 29

MASUDA NO IWAFUNE   7th century   Kashihara-shi, Mise-chō

This is a large stone structure approximately 11 meters in length, 8 meters in width, and 4.7 meters in height. The upper surface is flat, with a shallow trough and two square holes. Attempted explanations are various — for example, that it was a monument to commemorate the missionary and social activist Kōbō Daishi who undertook the work of constructing the Masuda Pond; that it was an ancient tomb; or that it was a platform for star divination — but its actual purpose remains a mystery. At present, the stone bears lattice-shaped indentations around its base which testify to the process used in flattening the outer surfaces.

MIROKU-ISHI
Height 2.5 meters   Asuka-mura, Oka

This stone is thought by some to have been used as a boundary marker between fields under the *jōri* land division system which was put into effect after the latter part of the 7th century. Others think it may have been used as part of a dam across the Asukagawa. In popular belief it has been taken as a "Miroku" (image of the Buddha of the future)

KAME-ISHI ("Tortoise Stone")
Length 3.6 meters   7th century
Asuka-mura, Tachibana

According to one theory, this stone was used to delineate *jōri* field boundaries, but its real purpose is unknown. Its exterior bears lattice-shaped indentations like those on the *Masuda no iwafune.*

← *Kame-ishi profile*

TATE-ISHI ("Standing Stone")
Asuka-mura, Oka (height 2.5 m)
Asuka-mura, Jōgo (height 1.9 m)
Asuka-mura, Toyura (height 2.9 m)

These stand at three locations in Asuka-mura. The *tate-ishi* on the grounds of the Amakashi-niimasu Jinja (in Toyura) is said to have been used in connection with land allotments prior to the *jōri* system. In addition to these worked stones, excavations have revealed a similarly shaped natural stone (height 1.6 m) which was stood on end along the bank of the Asukagawa east of the Kawaradera.

← *Map showing distribution of Asuka stones*

30

a Miroku-ishi   b "Mara-ishi" (phallic stone)

ASUKA KOFUN

ASUKA KOFUN

It was only after the beginning of the 6th century, when the Soga clan became power-ful, that burial tumuli began to be built in the Asuka region, which fell within the sphere of Soga influence. In the 7th century tumuli were built here by numerous powerful persons including emperors and others of the imperial clan.

The burial tumuli in the Asuka region are noteworthy for their use of quarried granite and also for their elaborately constructed stone chambers with lateral entrance passage-ways, a characteristic construction found also in the burial tumuli of the Kawachi-Asuka region, an area also known as "Nearer Asuka" (*chika-tsu-Asuka*) within the ancient province of Kawachi and including such areas of present-day Ōsaka-fu as Habikino-shi and Fujiidera-shi, but offering few other examples in the country as a whole. Influences from Korean burial tumuli are strikingly evident, testifying to the strong connections with newcomers from the continent.　⬆ *Stone coffin in Shōbuike Kofun*

⬅ *Aerial view of Ishibutai Kofun and artist's conception of original form.*

32
　　　　　　　　　　　a　Laterally entered chamber of Miyakozuka Kofun, Asuka-mura, Sakata

MARUYAMA KOFUN
Historical Site 6th century   Kashihara-shi, Mise-chō/Gojōno-chō

This is the largest of the *zenpō-kōenfun* (keyhole-shaped tumuli) in Nara prefecture. 318 meters in length, it is the sixth largest *kofun* in the country as a whole, and is said to be the largest built during the 6th century. It boasts a stone crypt which is longer (26 meters, including the lateral entrance passageway) than any other in Japan. There are two stone coffins. In earlier times it was mistakenly thought to be the jointly occupied mausoleum of Emperor Tenmu and Empress Jitō, who reigned at the end of the 7th century.   ⬆ *Aerial view of Maruyama Kofun*

b Laterally entered chamber of Maruyama Kofun (chart from Seiseki zushi, 1854).

b

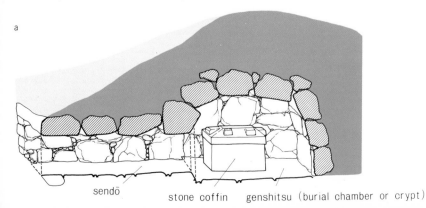

a

sendō   stone coffin   genshitsu (burial chamber or crypt)

一九山塚穴之圖

山陵志云有石棺二焉一在北
南面六在東西面圓以為其南
面天武也西面持統也

塚穴口南面

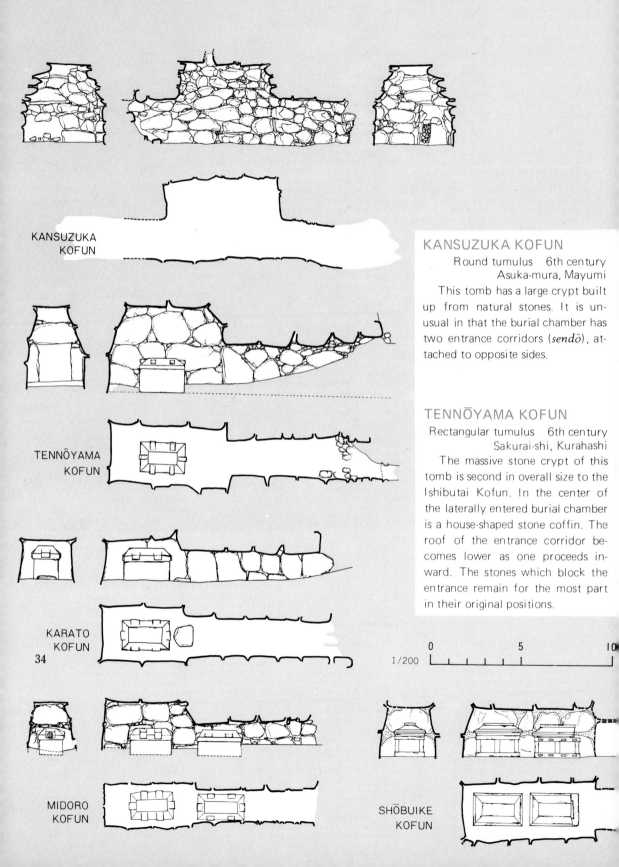

KANSUZUKA
KOFUN

TENNŌYAMA
KOFUN

KARATO
KOFUN

34

MIDORO
KOFUN

SHŌBUIKE
KOFUN

KANSUZUKA KOFUN

Round tumulus   6th century
Asuka-mura, Mayumi

This tomb has a large crypt built up from natural stones. It is unusual in that the burial chamber has two entrance corridors (*sendō*), attached to opposite sides.

TENNŌYAMA KOFUN

Rectangular tumulus   6th century
Sakurai-shi, Kurahashi

The massive stone crypt of this tomb is second in overall size to the Ishibutai Kofun. In the center of the laterally entered burial chamber is a house-shaped stone coffin. The roof of the entrance corridor becomes lower as one proceeds inward. The stones which block the entrance remain for the most part in their original positions.

1/200   0   5   10

ISHIBUTAI KOFUN

Special Historical Site   7th century   Asuka-mura, Shimanoshō

This tomb has an imposing laterally entered crypt built up from massive boulders. In comparison to other examples of ancient tombs which give similar impressions of great size due to the length of their crypts or the height of their ceilings, the Ishibutai crypt is, in overall size, the largest in Japan. The largest of its boulders, the one forming the southern part of the ceiling, is estimated to weigh 75 tons. The lower level of the two-tiered raised earth platform (*fūdo*) on which it rests is of rectangular shape, but since the upper level, together with the tumulus mound itself, was at some unknown point of time removed, it is impossible to judge whether the original tumulus was round or had square corners. Stones are emplaced around the outer edge of the *fūdo*, which is also surrounded by an empty moat. One theory has it that this was the tomb of Soga-no-Umako.

⬆ *Interior and exterior views of the Ishibutai stone crypt*

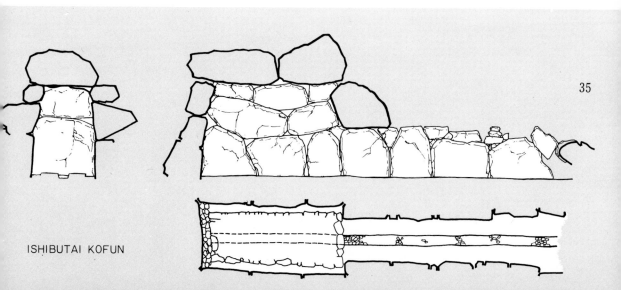

35

ISHIBUTAI KOFUN

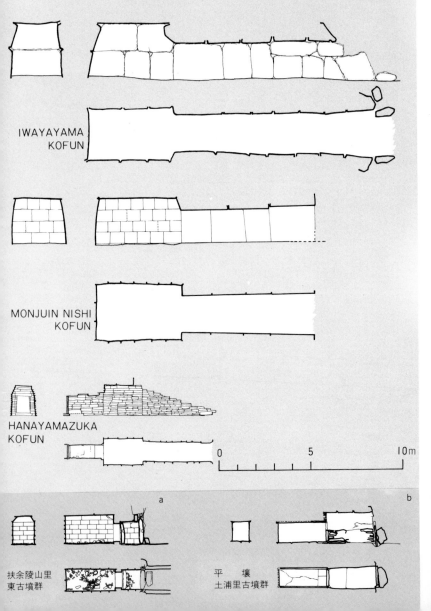

IWAYAYAMA KOFUN

MONJUIN NISHI KOFUN

HANAYAMAZUKA KOFUN

0   5   10m

a

b

扶余陵山里
東古墳群

平　壌
土浦里古墳群

MONJUIN NISHI-KOFUN

Special Historical Site   7th century
Sakurai-shi, Abe, Kanakura

The walls of the stone crypt are constructed of cut stones neatly emplaced in layers, each showing a different interface alignment. In three places, special pains were taken to give the impression that two stones were used when in reality a single stone was divided in the center by a vertical indentation to give the appearance of an interface. The ceiling is constructed of a single slab of stone, and the inner walls were designed to taper slightly inward toward the top. Influences from Korean *kofun* are evidenced in the overall structure, the method of stone emplacement and the relatively small difference in height between the burial chamber and entrance corridor. This tomb seems likely to have been built for a prominent personage of the Abe clan.

a Crypt of No. 1 tumulus, Tonggo tumulus group, Puyŏ Nŭngsanni,
b Crypt of No. 1 tumulus, Tumulus, T'op'ori tumulus group, P'yŏngyang, northern Korea.

...AYAYAMA KOFUN

Rectangular tumulus
7th century   Asuka-mura

This tomb has an exquisitely ...rked crypt of cut stones. The ...er sections of the chamber walls ...e inward, so that the ceiling is ...rower than the floor. As if in a ...culated effort to make the en...nce corridor give an exaggerated ...earance of depth, the entrance ...relatively high and wide, while ...passageway becomes both lower ...narrower as one proceeds in...d. Original plaster remains in ...stone interfaces.

*...Tumulus constructed in two
...ers (Iwayayama Kofun)
...Crypt of Iwayayama Kofun
...Cut stone with carved indentation
...(Monjuin Nishi-Kofun)*

...NAYAMAZUKA KOFUN

Historical Site
Round tumulus   7th century

This tomb has a laterally entered ...pt constructed of stones which ...e split in such a way as to re...ible *sen* (a sort of ceramic brick). ...ster was applied to the walls and ...ing. There is an additional rear ...mber at the back of the burial ...pt, and the slab of stone at the ...rance to this rear chamber was ...igned to open and close like a ...r. Strong influences from Ko...n *kofun* are recognized in both ...crypt design and the manner of ...e emplacement.

*...en-shaped cut stones and plaster
...anayamazuka Kofun)*

...ntrance to Monjuin Nishi-Kofun.
...ntrance to rear chamber
...f Hanayamazuka Kofun

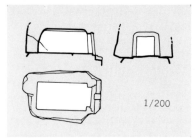

1/200

a   Oni no kawaya   b. Oni no manaita

ONI NO KAWAYA AND ONI NO MANAITA

7th century   Asuka-mura, Hirata, Noguchi

These are, respectively, a chamber-like enclosure hollowed out of a granite boulder and a cut stone designed to be laid under it as a sort of foundation and floor. Originally these two stones were, as in the case of the stone crypt of the *Gobōyama Kofun* in Yamato Kōriyama-shi, placed together as a set and covered with earth. However, the tumulus was at some time destroyed, and the stone forming the chamber-like section came to rest in an upturned position. In the course of time it came to be called the *Oni no kawaya* or *Oni no setchin* (both meaning "devil's privy"), while the floor stone came to be called the *Oni no manaita* ("devil's chopping board").

⬆ *Artist's reconstruction of crypt combining the two stones.*

38

a

b

KEGOSHIZUKA (ASAGAOZUKA)

Octagonal tumulus
7th century Asuka-mura, Koshi, Tsukamae

This crypt consists of two rooms hollowed out of a large block of porous limestone and was designed for the burial of a husband and wife. The floor is equipped with stone platforms on which to place the coffins. There was a double layer of stones blocking the doorway but they now lie overturned in front of the entrance. Of a number of cut stones which were placed around the perimeter of the original tumulus, nine remain. From their shapes and angles, one may speculate that the tumulus probably had eight sides. These cut stones placed on the tumulus perimeter draw on the same tradition as the *goseki* ("protective stones") placed around Korean *kofun* in the area of ancient Silla and elsewhere. Fragments of the two coffins, made of dried lacquer, have been excavated.

↑ *Stone chambers of Kegoshizuka tomb*

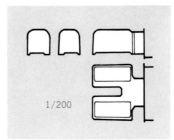

1/200

c Stone crypt from Gobōyama Kofun
d Doorway stones and entrance to crypt of Kegoshizuka tomb.
e Enameled metal coffin adornment excavated from Kegoshizuka Kofun

39

SHŌBUIKE KOFUN

Historical Site
7th century   Kashihara-shi, Gojōno-chō

Placed within the burial chamber are two carefully worked stone coffins of unusual shape. The inner surfaces of both sarcophagi are on all sides covered with lacquer-painted cloth. The burial chamber was constructed by juxtaposing natural stones, and was from the first designed to be especially deep in order to accomodate the two coffins set end to end.

MIDORO KOFUN

Historical Site
7th century   Gose-shi, Kose, Midoro

There are two tumuli in the same neighborhood which jointly bear the name *"Midoro Kofun."* In one of them there is, in addition to a stone coffin in the burial chamber proper, a second stone coffin in the entrance passageway. The latter is ornamented with a lotus flower design. Sixty meters to the north of this tomb is the other *Midoro Kofun* tumulus, which has a stately burial chamber likewise entered from the side. One theory has it that these two tumuli correspond to the *"Imaki no narabihaka"* (Imaki paired tombs) mentioned in the *Nihon shoki* as having been built by Sogano-Emishi and his son Iruka.

TRANSITION FROM *KOFUN* TO TOMBS WITH CREMATED REMAINS

Emperors and members of prominent clans continued to be buried in traditional-style *kofun* into the 7th century. However, together with Buddhism the practice of cremation was introduced, and in time the custom of cremating bodily remains came to be adopted by all, from the Emperor the nobility downward. The earliest written record of cremation in Japan refers to the priest Dōshō (d. 700, or the 4th year of the reign of Emperor Monmu). Already by that time large *kofun* (tumulus graves in the old style) were no longer being built, and the adoption of cremation further hastened the end of all tumulus building. Certain *kofun* exhibit a transitional character, as for example the *Nakaoyama Kofun* (Asuka-mura, Hirata), which was designed with an octagonal mound and a minutely worked stone crypt for the deposition of cremated bones.

MAUSOLEUM OF EMPEROR TENMU AND EMPRESS JITŌ

(Hinokuma no Ōuchi no Misasagi)

Empress Jitō (d. 702) was the first sovereign to be cremated, and her cremated remains were buried in the mausoleum of her husband Emperor Tenmu (d. 686). According to records of the Kamakura period, Tenmu's remains were placed in a dry lacquer casket, while those of Jitō lay in a silver vessel serving as a cinerary urn.

a Stone crypt of Nakaoyama Kofun (scale: 1/200)　　　b Ossuary unearthed at Okuyama　　　c Ossuary unearthed at Kamiide

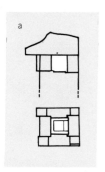

b c

TOMB INSCRIPTIONS

From the latter part of the 7th century through the end of the 8th century, it was a common practice, in imitation of Chinese custom, to place epitaphs (*boshi*) inside of tombs. These epitaphs consisted largely of chronological résumés of the lives of the deceased, recorded on silver or bronze strips of metal, rectangular tiles, cinerary urns, and the like.

The epitaph shown on the left of the page belongs to the tomb of Ono-no-Emishi, son of Ono-no-Imoko, poet and emissary to Sui China. From this inscription we learn that Emishi held the post of *Dajōkan* (prime minister) in the service of Emperor Tenmu, conjointly with the post of chief administrator (*chōkan*) of the Ministry of Justice (*kyōbushō*). He died in 677 (the 5th year of Tenmu's reign) and was posthumously awarded the rank of *daikin-jō*. The epitaph was unearthed from Ono-no-Emishi's burial site (an inhumation grave) on the hill behind the Sudō Jinja in Kyoto.

The illustrations at the bottom of the page show the cinerary urn and epitaph belonging to the tomb of *Fumi-no-Nemaro*, a general of immigrant descent who was active in support of Tenmu during the Jinshin Disturbance (672). He died in the year 700. The cinerary urn is made of green glass and was placed within a gilt bronze vessel. The inscription was placed inside a box, also of gilt bronze.

42

TAKAMATSUZUKA KOFUN

1/200

TAKAMATSUZUKA KOFUN
(Special Historical Si

This is the tumulus grave, located in the Hirata district of Asuka-mura, which becam
famous as the result of the excavation studies of 1972 which revealed its artistically ex
cuted wall frescoes. The tumulus, which is only 20 meters in diameter, is one of a sma
number of terminal period *kofun* which exhibit a distinctive construction process, four
only in Asuka, whereby the mound was built up in alternating layers of clay and sand. It
thought to have been built at some time between the end of the 7th century and the begi
ning of the 8th century.

The ceiling depicts star constellations (*seishuku*), and the surrounding walls depict th
sun, the moon, the four heavenly guardian gods (*shishin*), and earthly attendants, in such
way that a sort of miniature universe was formed for the purpose of accompanying the d
creased in his eternal sleep. The person for whom the grave was built is unknown, but th
decorations, grounded in Chinese concepts, are executed in a way that would befit the grav
of a nobleman.

⬆ *Takamatsuzuka Kofun before excavatio*

*Illustration, page 43.
Exterior of the south end of the Takamatsuzuka stone crypt, seen from cavity produce
during 1972 excavation. The construction of the tumulus through successively applied th
layers of clay and sand is well indicated. The indentations seen running lengthwise in th
foreground are the tracks left by rails which supported rollers used to transport the massiv
cut stones to the grave site. In the structure of the Takamatsuzuka stone crypt may be see
an abandonment of the earlier pattern of a stone chamber with a laterally attached entran
corridor (*yokoana-shiki sekishitsu*) and substitution of a pattern in which only a seale
coffin-shaped stone burial vault, or so-called *sekkan-shiki sekishitsu* remained, with r
passageway to the outside. The problematic wall frescoes are drawn on the inside surfaces
this crypt. (The photograph was taken after the south end of the crypt, found partially d
stroyed by grave robbers, had been repaired.)

➡ *Drawing of female on west wall of Takamatsuzuka cryp*

44

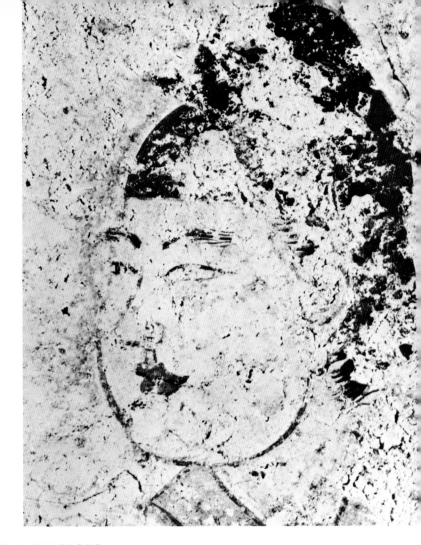

PEOPLE SHOWN IN THE FRESCOES

The males shown in the frescoes hold in their hands sunshades (*kinugasa*), chairs, and pouches containing swords and arrows, and also have pouches hung around their necks. The females carry round fans (*sashiba*), fly-swatters, Buddhist-related staffs of authority (*nyoi*), etc. Figures of both sexes depict handsomely attired attendants.

If one takes a close look at the facial outlines, it is seen that, in contrast to such drawings as the female portraitures in the Shōsōin, which were executed in lines which have a uniform thickness and were simply applied in a single stroke, the Takamatsuzuka portraitures were done in modulated lines, the brush having been restrained or brought to a stop at essential points. This sort of technique, and also the overall structuring of the group portraits, give eloquent testimony to the influence of Táng Chinese fresco art. ⬆ *Male depicted on east wall of Takamatsuzuka crypt (ultrared photography).*

a Táng female portraiture (Princess Yǒngtài Tomb fresco, near Sian, China).　　b　Nara Period female portraiture (from the torige dachionna byōbu, Shōsōin)

46

a

STAR CHARTS *(SEISHUKU)*

The ceiling of the Takamatsuzuka crypt is dotted with small bits of gold leaf, which are in turn joined in various patterns by reddish cinnabar lines in such a way as to represent star charts. The precision with which these were executed is unparalleled among similar charts found in Chinese and Korean fresco-bearing tumulus graves.

In China, such constellation charts were meant to give a representation in the heavenly bodies of the earthly political organization with the imperial court at its center. The ceiling of the Takamatsuzuka chamber is faithful to this type of Chinese concept, with the central sector of the heavens sketched in the center and 28 constellations (the so-called *nijū-hasshuku*) arranged on the four sides, seven to a side. This is an expression of the concept of rule over the entire universe by a "sovereign of the heavens" (*tentei*).

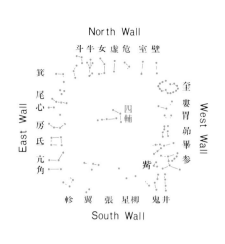

North Wall

斗牛女虚危 室壁

箕
尾
心   四輔
房
氏
亢
角

觜

奎婁胃昴畢参

West Wall

East Wall

軫翼張星柳 鬼井

South Wall

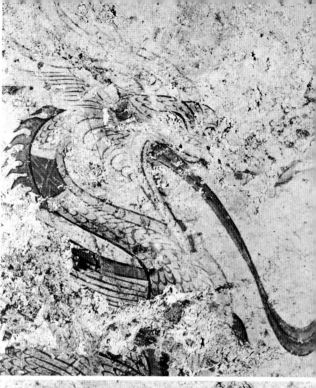

FOUR GUARDIAN SPIRITS *(SHISHIN)*

The four spirit deities guarding the four directions *(shishin)* were also frequently drawn on the walls of fresco-bearing tumulus graves in China and Korea. In their Japanese pronunciations, the names of these spirits are *Seiryū* ("blue-dragon") in the east, *Byakko* ("white tiger") in the west, *Suzaku* ("red bird") in the south, and *Genbu* ("black [snake] combatting [a tortoise]") in the north. The four guardian spirits on the walls of the *Takamatsuzuka* crypt, together with the star charts and the sun and moon with which they form a set, were designed to represent a universe with the buried personage at its center. The *Suzaku* figure which one would expect to see on the south wall no longer remains, having been destroyed at some point by grave robbers.

⬆ *Star charts*   ⬈ *Seiryū*   ➡ *Byakko*

c *Genbu*

47

b

c

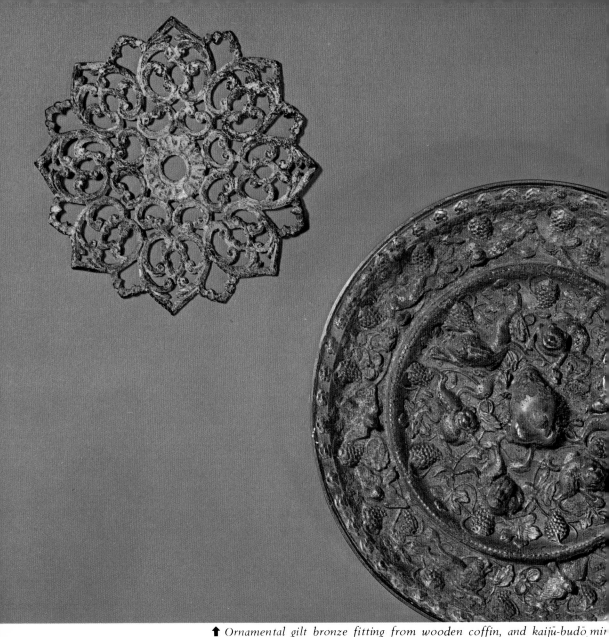

↑ *Ornamental gilt bronze fitting from wooden coffin, and kaijū-budō mi*

OTHER TAKAMATSUZUKA REMAINS

The interior of the Takamatsuzuka crypt was found in a state of disorder due to a past break-in by grav robbers. However, there remained such artifacts as a wooden coffin painted with black lacquer and orna mented with metal nails and fittings, a Táng Chinese mirror whose reverse was worked in a so-called *kaijū budō* pattern (depicting animals, birds, grapevines, etc.), and ornamental fittings for a Táng style sword. As general rule, in terminal period tumuli dating from around the same time as the Takamatsuzuka Kofun grav goods, while of superior workmanship, are relatively few both in number and variety. From a study of th bones in the Takamatsuzuka coffin, it is judged that the buried person was a male of tall stature between 4 and 60 years old. Judged from the grave goods and the content of the frescoes, he was likely a prominen member of the imperial or some other high-ranking clan.

48

a   Ornamental silver sword fittin

a

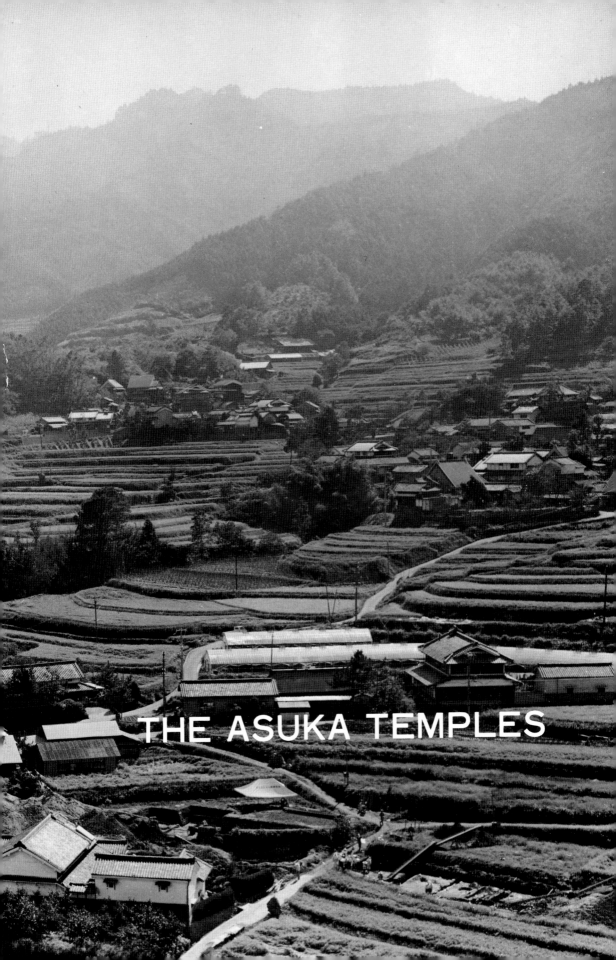

THE ASUKA TEMPLES

THE ASUKA TEMPLES

It is thought that Buddhism was first publicly introduced in our country in the year 538 (seventh year of Emperor Kinmei's reign), when King Sŏngmyŏng of the southwestern Korean state of Paekche (Japanese pronunciation: Kudara) presented Buddhist images and sutras to the Japanese court. The Soga clan, possessed of wealth and influence at that time, gave its positive support to the new religion, and Buddhism gradually spread among the imperial house and other influential families. Construction of Japan's first full-scale temple, the Asukadera, was begun in 588 (first year of Emperor Sushun's reign), a half-century after Buddhism's first arrival. Construction of the Asukadera was sponsored by the Soga clan, which had one year previously (in 587) defeated the Mononobe clan in an armed encounter and thus established its own political power more firmly.

Already in the years immediately following the initial introduction of Buddhism around the middle of the 6th century, Buddhist images had come to be revered within certain wealthy and influential households. Following the example of the Asukadera, other full-scale religious institutions were in due course to be built by these same families and by the imperial house. According to the *Nihon shoki*, in 680 (the 9th year of Emperor Tenmu's reign) there were within the capital district (i.e., the Asuka and Fujiwara region) 24 temples, the majority of them semi-private "clan temples" (*ujidera*) built by certain wealthy families.

With the advent of Tenmu's reign (672~686), there came into being a system of designating certain temples as "official temples" (*kanji*), for purposes of exercising a certain amount of coordination over the activities of priests and nuns and for purposes of coordinating nationwide Buddhist festivities and observances. The most important *kanji* were the "Four Great Temples" of the day, namely, Daikandaiji, Yakushiji, Asukadera and Kawaradera. Most of the temples of the time were called after local place names, but in addition bore Chinese-style designations (*hōgō*).

 Paekche (southwest Korean) roof tile and roof tile from the Asukadera
 Excavation at site of Sakatadera

50

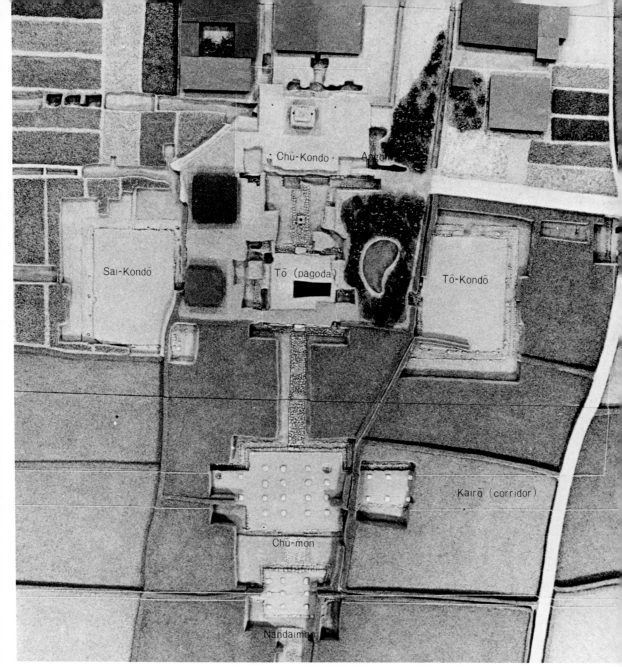

Model of original ground plan of Asukadera, as determined from archaeological remains.

a Excavation and layout of temple at Ch'ŏngamni (清岩里), P'yŏngyang, Korea.

Chū-kondō

Octagonal Pavilion

Sai-kondō

Tō-kondō

Chūmon

ASUKADERA (HŌKŌJI · Gangōji)

The Asukadera, built by Soga-no-Umako, is representative of the large temples of the first half of the 7th century and provides a good indication of the Buddhist culture of the time. Excavation studies reveal that it was originally a great temple covering an area some 200 meters on a side and having in its central portion three "golden halls" (*kondō*, sometimes translated "main hall" or "image hall") clustered around a pagoda (*tō*). It is known that workmen from Paekche (Kudara) were engaged in its construction, and the influence of contemporary Korean Buddhist culture is evidenced in the layout of the buildings and connecting passageways, and even in the designs on the roof tiles.

⬆ *Excavated sites of the middle gate (above) and the east kondō.*

⬆ *Excavations at Asukadera, viewed from the east.*

RELIQUARY AND WOODEN BOX FROM THE ASUKADERA PAGODA

The pagoda of the Asukadera was lost to fire in 1196, and the relics (*shari*) buried beneath it were excavated the following year. A newly made reliquary was placed in a wooden box and buried about 2 meters above the central foundation stone (itself some 3 meters below the surface). An inscription running around the sides of this box tells us that the pagoda burned in the year Kenkyū 7 (i.e., 1196, by modern reckoning), and that it had belonged to the "Moto Gangōji." The religious establishment originally attached to the Asukadera was moved in the early 8th century to the Heijō (Nara) capital and newly established as the Gangōji, and it was in this way that the temple buildings remaining in Asuka had come to be known as the Moto (meaning "former" or "original") Gangōji.

↗ *Reliquary from beneath Asukadera pagoda.*

← *Iron armor, originally buried together with Buddhist relics under the Asukadera pagoda (late 6th century).*

c
「御庄司入阿
此本元興寺」

b
「寺僧玄昭明暁
依建久七年」

a~c

Wooden box for the reliquary. Photographs (b) and (c) show part of the above-mentioned inscription. (There is no logical sequence of meaning in the writing as shown on these two sides of the box taken alone.)

54

a

c

b

OBJECTS BURIED UNDER THE ASUKA-DERA PAGODA

Soga-no-Umako in 593 had several Buddhist relics (*busshari*) placed within the central foundation stone (*tōshinso*), upon which stood the pagoda's center shaft. It is noteworthy that various objects not specifically connected with Buddhism were buried there at the same time, and that these other artifacts are nearly identical to those buried in tumulus graves (*kofun*) of the same period. This finding provides a good perspective on the state of transition whereby, during a time of continued *kofun*-building, Buddhism was beginning to spread among the various *gōzoku*.

↑ *Central foundation stone upon excavation*
← *Buried objects (Asukadera) (See page 98)*

ASUKA DAIBUTSU

This was the main object of worship (*honzon*) in the Asukadera's original *chū-kondō* (central main hall). It was cast in 609 (the 17th year of Empress Suiko's reign) by the master of Buddhist sculpture (*busshi*) Kuratsukuri-no-Tori, son of a Korean immigrant. It is the oldest extant Buddhist image in Japan whose date of construction is definitely known. Repairs and alterations from later times are clearly in evidence, but in such features as the elongated face and the shape of the eyes may be seen the original characteristics of the *Tori-shiki* (Tori style) Buddhist imagery shared also by the Shaka triad at the Hōryūji. The granite base is original, as are the socketed stands (*hozoana*) presently placed on either side and serving to support the flanking attendant figures. Comparing the Asuka Daibutsu with the Hōryūji Shaka triad, one is reminded of the power possessed by the Soga family, who were able to commission the building of a *jōroku-zō*, or what was considered to be a full-scale image, one *jō* and six *shaku* (or about 4.8 meters) high — several times larger than the central figure of the Hōryūji triad.

← *Head of Asuka Daibutsu*

Shijūhattai-butsu
("The Forty-eight Buddhist Images")
These are an assemblage of 59 miniature gilt-bronze Buddhist sculptures, produced at various times from the Asuka through the Tempyō Periods. They were at one time in the possession of the Hōryūji. Among them are several which had been transferred there from the Tachibanadera in the 11th century. They are presently housed in the Tokyo National Museum. The number "forty-eight," while inaccurate as a name for the present collection, seems to have been chosen as a reflection of the "48 vows of Amida."

56

a

b.

OTHER BUDDHIST IMAGES OF THE ASUKA PERIOD

In art history, the term "Asuka Period" denotes the time between the introduction of Buddhism and approximately the middle of the 7th century, while the latter half of the 7th century is denoted by the term "Hakuhō Period." Buddhist images of the Asuka Period, so defined, were made primarily by craftsmen of continental immigrant stock, and the period's mainstream works were the *Tori-shiki* Buddhist images such as the Asuka Daibutsu, the Shaka triad (produced for the Hōryūji *kondō* in 623 by Kuratsukuri-no-Tori), the Guze Kannon in the Hōryūji Yumedono, etc. "*Tori-shiki*" Buddhist images were influenced by the Buddhist art of the Northern Wèi Period in China and exhibit such characteristics as a marked frontality, almond-shaped eyes, upward-turned crescent-shaped lips, and symmetrically arranged folds in the clothing. Besides the *Tori-shiki* images, there also remain from the Asuka Period such images as the Kudara Kannon at the Hōryūji and the "boddhisattva half-inclined in meditation" (*bosatsu hankazō*) at the Cyūgūji (part of the Hōryūji)

BRONZE FIGURES OF LADY MAYA AND HEAVENLY ATTENDANTS *(TENNIN)*   (Part of the *Shijūhattai-butsu*)   first half of 7th century

This is an ensemble representing the scene of the birth of Shakyamuni (Japanese pronunciation: *Shaka*) from beneath the arm of his mother, the Lady Maya. Since the earliest days of the Buddhist faith in India, objects of Buddhist reverence in various parts of Asia have included, in addition to images representing the person of the historical Shakyamuni in idealized form, paintings and sculptures recalling the vicissitudes of the Buddha's life as given in the traditional accounts *(butsuden)*. In Japan, however, the latter type of Buddhist art is unusual.

↑ *Lady Maya and tennin*

BRONZE NIMBUS *(KŌHAI)*   (One of the *Shijūhattai-butsu*)

This is the halo for a Shaka image and was produced by Ō En son (Chinese pronunciation: Wáng Yánsùn), perhaps a continental immigrant, in a year which, as designated in the Chinese sixty-year cycle by the characters *kolin*, could represent in this case either the year 594 or the year 654. It is a so-called *ikkōsanzon-shiki* halo, designed to enfold both a central image and attendant Boddhisattvas flanking it on either side. Nimbuses which, like this one, have attached to them small Buddhas and heavenly attendants *(tennin)* are very often used with Buddhist images that, like the Asuka Daibutsu or the Shaka Nyorai in the Hōryūji Kondō, draw on traditions of the Northern Wèi.

➡ *Bronze nimbus*

a   Miroku Bosatsu, Chūgūji   b   Kudara Kannon, Hōryūji   c   Miroku Bosatsu, Kōryūji.

58

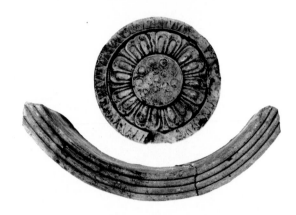

KAWARADERA (Gufukuji)

The Kawaradera is considered to have had its beginning during the reign of Emperor Tenji (662~671), when the grounds of the Asuka Kawara-no-miya were converted to a temple. It was from the following reign of Emperor Tenmu, when "official temples" (*kanji*) were established and given economic support by the country at large, that Buddhism, centering around these "official temples," came to flourish as the national religion. The Kawaradera, designated as one of the "official temples," was moreover counted among the "Four Great Temples" (see page 50). Excavation studies have determined that the temple had a stately arrangement of buildings (*garan*) whose architecture drew on influences from early Táng China. There was a pagoda, two golden halls, and priests' quarters surrounding the central grounds on three sides.

At present the original ground plan of the halls and pagoda is being restored. Agate-marble foundation stones from the central golden hall remain. ⬆ *Roof tiles, Kawaradera*
⬇ *Kawaradera site under excavation, viewed from the west* ➡ *Artist's reconstruction of the Kawaradera, viewed from the southwest.* ↖ *Remains of foundations of Kawaradera pagoda.*
Kawaradera site after being restored to original ground plan. Across the Asukagawa (river), near the top of the photograph may be seen the reputed site of the Asuka Itabuki-no-miya, its original ground plan restored.

↑ *Site of west golden hall, Kawaradera.*

↓ *Site of middle gate and corridor, Kawaradera.*

Weary of both oceans
Living and death
How I do miss that ebbtide hill   *Man'yōshū 3849*

In This World's restless borrowed cabin
We live on, yet knowing not
Our land of destination   *Man'yōshū 3850*

The above two poems on "the impermanence of the world" are said to have been inscribed on a *yamatokoto* (Japanese lyre) once kept at the Kawaradera.

olution of temple ground plans (scale: 1/3000)

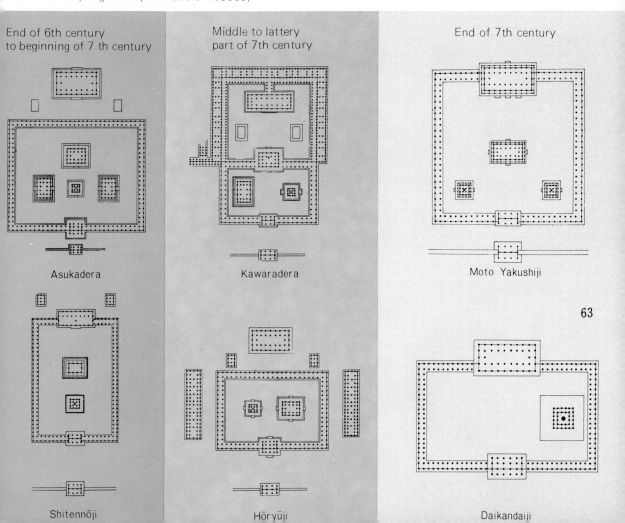

End of 6th century
to beginning of 7 th century

Middle to lattery
part of 7th century

End of 7th century

Asukadera

Kawaradera

Moto Yakushiji

63

Shitennōji

Hōryūji

Daikandaiji

MOTO YAKUSHIJI

Special Historical Site
Kashihara-shi, Kidono-chô

Emperor Tenmu, praying that his wife (later Empress Jitō) would recover from illness, laid the plans for this temple dedicated to the "healing Buddha" Yakushi. The temple, for the most part completed in 698 (the 2nd year of Emperor Monmu's reign), adopted a novel ground plan for the constituent buildings (*garan*), with both an east and west pagoda in front of the golden hall. Rivaling in size and prestige the Daikandaiji in the eastern precinct (*sakyō*) of Fujiwara-kyō (see page 16), this temple in the western precinct (*ukyo*) was a further enhancement to the stately elegance of the Fujiwara capital.

Even after the temple's religious establishment was transferred to Heijō-kyō (Nara) in the early 8th century, a part of the original buildings remained in use until the early part of the Heian period (after the capital had been further moved to Kyoto at the end of the 8th century). In this way, the remaining temple came to be called the Moto ("original") Yakushiji, in contradistinction to the new Yakushiji as reestablished in Nara.

↖ *Foundation stones at site of Moto Yakushiji golden hall*

↑ *Site of the west pagoda of the Moto Yakushiji, as viewed from the site of the east pagoda*

Tiles from Moto Yakushiji (a, b), and from Daikandaiji (c, d)

64

a
b

c
d

DAIKANDAIJI

Historical Site
Asuka-mura, Koyama

This temple, also known as the "Takechi Daiji," was the forerunner of the Daianji of Heijō-kyō (Nara). From historical references, it appears already to have taken form to a certain extent in the last years of Tenmu's reign (around 682), but construction work continued until the beginning years of the 8th century. During the Fujiwara-kyō period, it was designated as chief among the "official temples." It had a 7-storey pagoda and was the largest temple in the Asuka region. It was lost to fire in 711, the year following the removal of the capital to Heijō (Nara).

Today one may see the remains of foundation platforms from the pagoda and golden hall (*kondō*). The dimensions of the golden hall (53 meters from east to west; 28.5 meters from north to south) have become known from excavation studies. Also discovered were such artifacts as hanging metal fittings for wind-bells, and other ornamental metal objects attached to corner rafters. ↓ *Sites of pagoda (foreground) and golden hall under excavation (background).*

↑ *Metal ornament attached to corner rafter, from site of Daikandaiji golden hall (artist's reconstruction).*

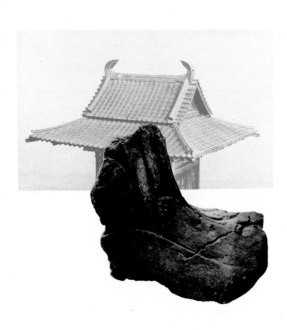

YAMADADERA (Jōdoji)

Sakurai-shi, Yamada

Construction of this large temple was begun in 641 (the 13th year of Emperor Jomei's reign) by Soga-no-Kurayamada Ishikawamaro, a cousin of Soga-no-Iruka. It was one of the clan temples (*ujidera*) the construction of which was then in vogue among the various wealthy families of the time. Although Ishikawamaro participated in the Taika coup d'état (which involved the murder of his cousin Iruka) and was subsequently appointed Minister of the Right (*udaijin*), in 649 (Taika 5) he came under suspicion for allegedly plotting rebellion. The same year he committed suicide in the still unfinished clan temple. He was posthumously absolved of the earlier suspicions, and the building of the Yamadadera was continued with help from the imperial house and completed in the latter half of the 7th century. The Yamadadera is thought to have had a ground plan with gate, pagoda, golden hall and lecture hall arranged in a line from south to north, respectively.

⬆ *Ornamental ridge-end tile (shibi) from Yamadadera,*
with roof of Tamamushi shrine (Hōryūji) in background.
⬆ *Foundation stones at site of lecture hall.*

a Wind acceptor of a bell from Yamadadera pagoda

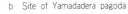
b Site of Yamadadera pagoda

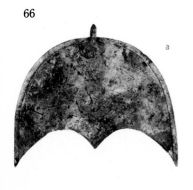
a

b

BUDDHA HEAD FROM THE YAMADADERA

The image of Nyorai (the historical Buddha) which was completed in 685 (the 14th year of Tenmu's reign) and served as the main object of worship in the Yamadadera lecture hall was in 1186 transferred to the east golden hall of the Kōfukuji in Nara. Later it was caught in a fire disaster and only the head remained. Drawing on early Táng influences, it exhibits such characteristic features of early Hakuhō Period Buddhist images as the bright expression and boyish countenance, the eyebrows drawn out in a long arc, and the elongated narrow eyes. The boddihisattvas which stand today on both sides of the main image of worship in the Kōfukuji east golden hall were originally the lateral attendant figures for this image when it stood in the Yamadadera. After the beginning of the latter half of the 7th century, such large-scale 3-piece displays (*sanzonbutsu*), in which the attendant figures assume a considerable degree of independence, came to be created in large number, even in clan temples.

HAKUHŌ PERIOD BUDDHIST IMAGES

Buddhist images of the Hakuhō Period show a departure from the somewhat stiff feeling produced by the images of the earlier Asuka Period. The early Hakuhō images typically have plump expressions reminding one of children, although under the continuing influence of Táng art, they develop into imposing pieces with adult bearing. Well-known and representative images of the period are the Buddha head from the Yamadadera with its boyish face. During this period in art history (i.e., latter half of the 7th century), the techniques of sculpture developed greatly in the hands of craftsmen from among newly arriving continental immigrants. With the production of images in clay and dry lacquer, and with the appearance of Buddhist figures modeled from stone, cast on tiles, or hammered out on metal using reusable casts, there was a notable diversification in the types of materials employed. Also, there emerged during this period a richer diversity in modes of expression, with such works as Nyorai images seated on chairs and standing boddhisattvas with inclining waists.

➡ *Yumechigai Kannon, Hōryūji*

⬅ *Amida triad bearing inscription "image belonging to Lord Yamada" (possibly Soga-no-Kurayamada Ishikawamaro). It forms part of the Shijūhattai-butsu.*

SEMI-INCLINED BODDHISATTVA FIGURES (*BOSATSU HANKAZŌ*) IN BRONZE

During the Asuka and Hakuhō Periods, there were produced many images of Miroku Bosatsu (the Boddhisattva Maitreya, sometimes rendered in English as "the Buddha of the future"), represented in a "half-inclined in meditation" posture.

The illustration at the upper right is a Miroku Bosatsu image made in 666 in supplication for the recovery from illness of Empress Saimei. It is housed in the Yachūji (Ōsaka-fu, Habikino-shi). Although a Hakuhō Period production, it retains much that is suggestive of Asuka Period imagery.

The *bosatsu hankazō* shown in figure (e) below has a number of features characteristic of Buddhist imagery of the latter half of the 7th century. These include, for example, the delicate facial features; the type of head ornament known as *sanmen tōshoku*, and the generous size of the lotus petals at the base. It is said to have been originally housed within the body of the Nyoirin Kannon which is the main object of worship at the Okadera.

Inscription: Yamada-donozō ("image belonging to Lord Yamada")
Miroku Butsu in main hall (Taimadera)
Amida Triad, known as Lady Tachibana's Triad (Hōryūji)
Semi-inclined boddhisattva (one of Shijūhattai-butsu).
Semi-inclined boddhisattva (Okadera)
Standing boddhisattva (one of Shijūhattai-butsu)

70

HOKKE SESSŌZU

This is a cast metal plaque with a scene of Shaka delivering a sermon. In suc
features as the miniature stamped Buddha images (*oshidashibutsu*) attached t
parts of the surface, and the hairline engravings of heavenly attendants (*tennin*
around the lower edge, one sees that a variety of metalworking techniques wer
imaginatively and skillfully employed. In its lower section, there is an inscriptio
to the effect that it was made for the emperor in the "year of the dog" (in th
case, either 686 or 698) by the priest Dōmyō and colleagues. According to som
accounts, this bronze plaque was originally emplaced as an object of worship i
a stone chamber or grotto on a hill west of the Hasedera.

CLAY FIGURES

The variety in the types of materials used for Buddhist images in the Hakuhō Period is reflected in many forms, including the clay figures (*sozō*) which have been unearthed from the sites of Asuka temples. Such figures were produced by applying clay to a wooden core and were then finished by the addition of surface coloring. Besides the famous clay productions from the 8th century which have been handed down in the Hōryūji, Tōdaiji and Kōfukuji, earlier clay figures from the 7th century have been found in Asuka, at such locations as the hill behind the Kawaradera, the Tachibanadera, the Tachibedera and the Moto Yakushiji.

Fragment of clay lotus pedestal from Tachibanadera.
c Other fragments of clay figures from Tachibanadera.
Clay figure from Tachibedera.

↑ *Clay figure unearthed on hill behind Kawaradera.*

b   c   d

SENBUTSU

Buddhist images stamped in relief on *sen* (brick-like tiles) were in vogue during the Hakuhō Period and frequently decorated the interiors of temple halls and pagodas. One may see a reflection of this trend in the tiny Buddhist images stamped from the reverse side onto the gilt bronze foil that covers the interior of the shutters and inner walls of the Tamamushi miniature shrine (*zushi*) at the Hōryūji. The stamped brick images (*senbutsu*) have designs in common with other stamped or rock-carved Buddhist images and also with the wall paintings in the Hōryūji golden hall, exuding a florid atmosphere that recalls influences from early Táng China. They typically have *sanzon* designs (Shaka attended by two boddhisattvas), or show other grouped figures, or flights to or from extraterrestial abodes.

⬆ *Senbutsu from the hill behind Kawaradera.*
　　a Senbutsu from Yamadadera
　　b c Senbutsu from Minami Hokkeji

➡ *Senbutsu from Tachibanadera*
d　Senbutsu from Tachibanadera
e　Cast for stamping senbutsu

a

b

Tamamushi miniature shrine at the Hóryūji. The interior walls and shutters, decorated with embossed Buddhist images (*oshidashibutsu*) on gilt bronze foil, give an idea of the way full-scale rooms ornamented with *senbutsu* must have looked.

Fragment of *senbutsu* from Kidera (see page 81). This figure, cast in unusually high relief, possesses a brightness characteristic of Hakuhō Period Buddhist imagery.

a No. 10 wall painting of Hōryūji Kondō.
b Buddhist image carved in relief on stone (sekibutsu) at Ishiidera.
c Buddhist design embossed on foil (oshidashi-butsu), at Hōryūji.

74

a

b

c

75

RYOKUYŪ HAMON-SEN   7th century   Kawaradera

These are fragments of tiles covered with green glaze and showing wave patterns (*hamon*) in relief. They were probably spread atop platforms (*shumidan*) for Buddhist objects inside temple halls and meant to represent "lotus ponds of the pure land," similar to the lotus pond depicted under the Buddhist images within the Tachibana miniature shrine at the Hōryūji. In Japan, these are the oldest extant baked clay objects which are coated with green glaze (*ryokuyū*).

TENNIN-SEN AND HŌŌ-SEN   7th century   Okadera and Minami Hokkeji

In addition to the brick-like tiles (*sen*) from the Hakuhō Period which depict images of the Buddha, there remain two others, both at one time in the possession of the Okadera, depicting a *tennin* (heavenly attendant) and a *hōō* (phoenix-like mythical bird), respectively. An intricately constructed *senbutsu* fragment (see illustration, page 77) unearthed from the site of an abandoned temple at Natsumi, Mie-ken, shows miniature *sen* ornamented with figures of *tennin*, worshippers, incense burners and lions, surrounding the base of a *shumidan* (platform for a Buddhist image). The extant *tennin-sen* and *hōō-sen* were perhaps used in the same way around the base of a full-scale *shumidan*.

➡ *Top and bottom right: tennin-sen and hōō-sen*

a Lotus pond of the Tachibana miniature shrine

b Ryokuyū hamon-sen

c Senbutsu fragment from site of abandoned temple at Natsumi, Mie-ken.

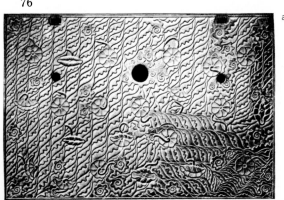

a

77

Autumn *hagi* on the hills rounded by Asukagawa's passing
In today's falling rain will it be all scattered and gone?

Man'yōshū 1557

(composed by Tajihi-no-Kunihito at
a banquet in the private apartment of
a nun of Toyuradera)

TOYURADERA   Asuka-mura, Toyura

It is said that this temple had its beginning after Empress
Suiko moved in 603 (the 11th year of her reign) from the Toyura-
no-miya to the Oharida-no-miya, following which move Soga-no-
Umako, having been granted possession of the former palace
at Toyura, made it into a temple. Originally it was a nunnery.
Tradition has it that the Mukuharadera, built by Umako's father
Iname, was located in one corner of its grounds. It also seems
likely that the "north pagoda" referred to in historical accounts
as having been built by Umako in 585 (the 14th year of Emperor
Bidatsu's reign) on a hill known as Ōno-no-oka, was in the same
vicinity. Archaeological remains of temple buildings and a pagoda
have been confirmed in the neighborhood which still today is
known by the name Toyura. These include the central foundation
stone *(tōshinso)* of the pagoda belonging to the Toyuradera
proper, which was erected in 634 (the 6th year of Emperor
Jomei's reign).   ← *Site of Toyuradera (present-day Kōgenji)*

TACHIBEDERA (Jōrinji)
Historical Site   Asuka-mura, Tachibe (Dōyama)

This temple is said to have been built by Shōtoku Taishi.
Its remains lie within the precincts of the present-day Kasuga
Jinja (not to be confused with the larger shrine of the same
name in Nara). Construction was probably commenced during
the first half of the 7th century. Diagonally in back of the
vestiges of a pagoda, there remain traces of a temple hall *(dō)*.
Excavations have revealed fragments from the head and neck
of clay boddhisattva images unearthed from the site of the
pagoda, which has a deeply buried foundation stone.

← *Site of Tachibedera (Jōrinji), seen from a distance*

a Tile from Tachibedera
b Tile from Toyuradera
c Tile from Sakatadera

78

a   b

The young girl Hanari whom I once took to sleep
In one of the long narrow shelters at Tachibanadera
I wonder if she'll by now have tied her hair?

Man'yōshū 3822 (anonymous)

SAKATADERA (Kongōji)

Asuka-mura, Iwaido

This temple is said (in the *Nihon shoki*) to have been built at the bequest of Tasuna (father of Kuratsukuri-no-Tori), who in 587 promised its construction in supplication for Emperor Yōmei's recovery from illness. However, other references say the actual construction was undertaken by Tori. This temple, which served as the "clan temple" (*ujidera*) of the immigrant Kuratsukuri clan, is the oldest such temple on record as having been built by continental immigrants. It seems originally to have been a nunnery. Excavations have revealed a well, drainage ditches, and tiles from the early 7th century. ➡ *Remains of well, Sakatadera*

TACHIBANADERA (Bodaiji)

Asuka-mura, Tachibana

This was originally a nunnery, said to have been built on the site of Shōtoku Taishi's birth. Most large temples of the time faced southward, but the Tachibanadera was unusual in that it faced east, with central gate, pagoda, golden hall and lecture hall aligned in a straight line from east to west. The central foundation stone for the pagoda is designed so as to accomodate three additional shafts serving as supports for the center shaft. This design is similar to that of the central foundation stone of the pagoda at the site of the Wakakusadera excavated on the grounds of the Hōryūji. ➡ *Central foundation stone of pagoda, Tachibanadera*

d Tachibanadera photographed after a snowfall
e Tile from Tachibanadera

d

f

HINOKUMADERA

Asuka-mura, Hinokuma

This temple is thought to have been built in the latter half of the 7th century by the Yamato no Aya clan, descendents of Korean immigrants settled in the Hinokuma district. The foundation stones of its halls and pagoda remain within the precincts of the Omiashi Jinja, whose tutelary spirit is that of Achi no Ōmi, reputed founder of the Yamato no Aya clan in Japan. Above the remains of the original pagoda there is a miniature 13-storey stone pagoda (*sekitō*) built at the close of the Heian Period (12th century).

⬆ *Tōshinso of Hinokumadera original pagoda*   ⬆ *Reliquaries from site of Hinokumadera pagoda*   ⬅ *13-storey sekitō at site of Hinokumadera, and foundation stone at site of Kuriharadera*

ŌKUBODERA

Kashihara-shi, Ōkubo

Only the central foundation stone of the pagoda *(tōshinso)* remains, together with some tiles from the middle part of the 7th century which are similar to those from the Yamadadera. The name of this temple appears in the *Nihon shoki* among references to events of the year 686. It was perhaps a "clan temple" (*ujidera*) of the Ōkubo clan, descendents of continental immigrants.

KURIHARADERA

Asuka-mura, Hirata (Kurihara)

Judged from the tile designs, this temple appears to have been founded in the early 8th century. Foundation stones remain. It is thought by some that in the Kurihara region there lived descendents of immigrants who came in the mid-5th century from "Kure-no-kuni" (possibly the state of Wu in east-central China, or possibly Korea). It was in this region that the cremation of the priest Dōshō was performed (see page 41).

a Tile from Hinokumadera

a   b   c

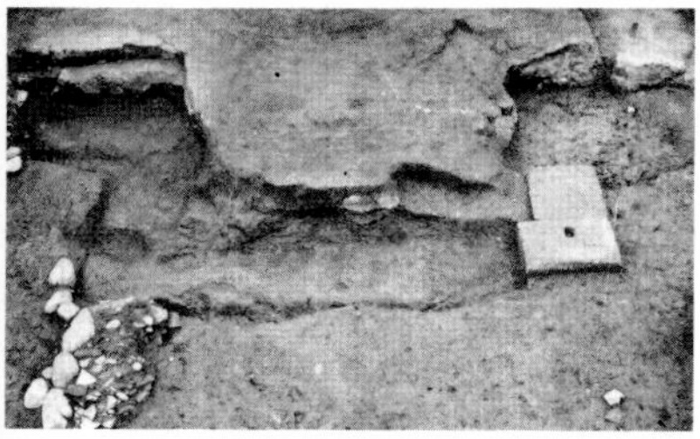

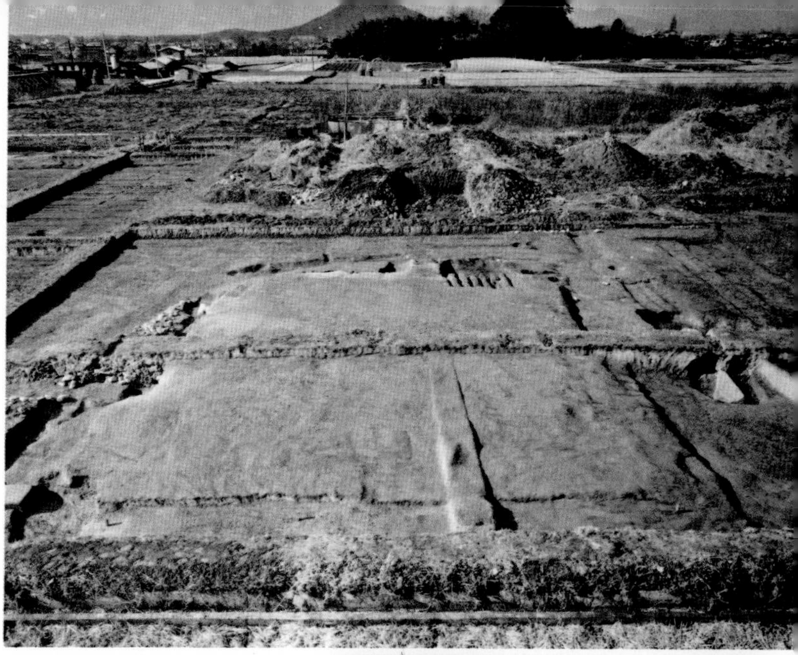

KIDERA

Asuka-mura, Koyama

This was the "clan temple" (*ujidera*) of the Ki clan, a wealthy and influential family during the Asuka and Nara periods. The site is within the confines of the Fujiwara-kyō (completed 694), but the founding of the temple dates back to the reign of Emperor Tenji (662~671). Excavations have confirmed the extent of the original temple grounds as well as remains of the surrounding temple wall, great south gate (***nandaimon***), central gate (*chūmon*), golden hall (***kondō***), and lecture hall (***kōdō***). The scale of the ***kondō*** approximates that of the ***kondō*** at the Kawaradera. At the ***kondō*** site were found ***senbutsu*** whose designs in high relief give a vivid impression of three-dimensionality.

⬆ *Remains of a staircase at site of Kidera kondō*

⬈ *Site of Kidera kondō, viewed from the west.*

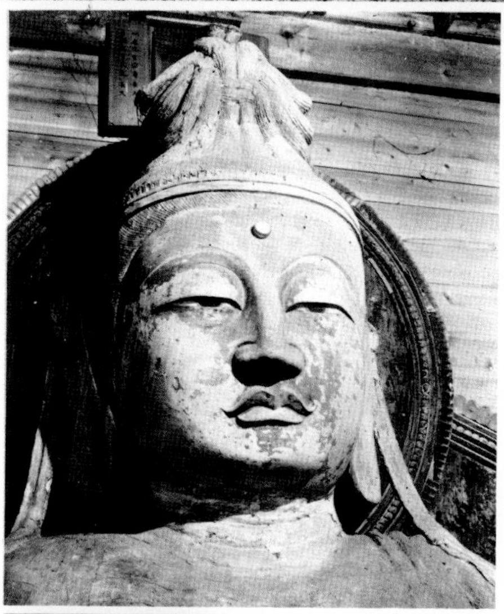

OKADERA (Ryūgaiji)

Asuka-mura, Oka

Historical records tell us that this temple was constructed by Gien in the latter half of the 7th century. Tiles from that time have been unearthed at the Harita Jinja which adjoins the grounds of the present-day Okadera on the west, and it is thought that here was the site of the original temple. Gien (died 728) was a high priest born in Asuka. Among his pupils were such social and religious activists of the Nara period as Genbō, Dōji, Gyōki, Ryōben and Dōkyō. The statue of Nyoirin Kannon (Sanskrit: Cintamanicakra) which is the Okadera's main object of worship (***honzon***) was made in the 8th century and is the largest clay image in Japan, with a height of 4.5 meters.

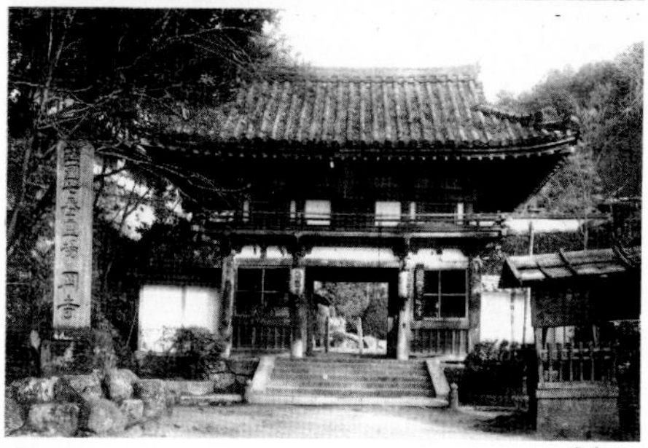

⬈ *Nyoirin Kannon, Okadera* ➡ *Two-storeyed gate (rōmon) at Okadera, built 1612*

Tile from Ōkubodera c Tile from Kuriharadera d e Tiles from Kidera f g Tiles from Okadera

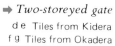

d e

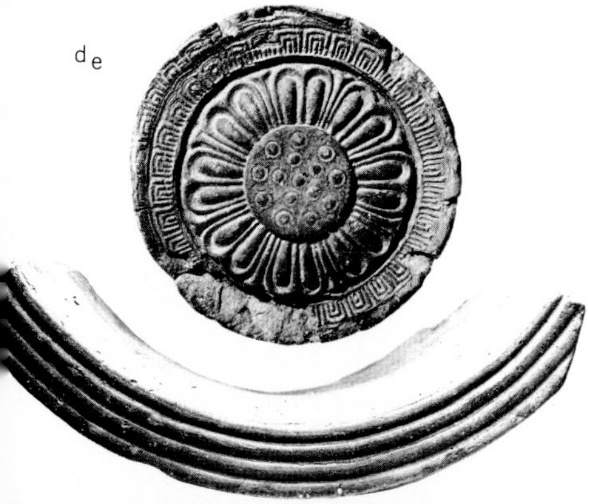

f g

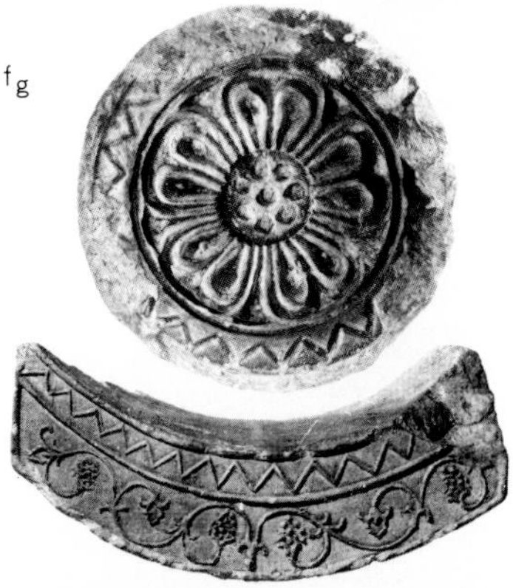

KUMEDERA   Kashihara-shi, Kume

Since olden times this temple has been confused with the Okuyama Kumedera (see below), and the circumstances of its founding are unclear. Tile designs suggest that the temple was likely already in existence in the latter half of the 7th century. It is known to have flourished during the early Heian period. Remains include a rarely seen assemblage of boulders used as foundation stones for the pagoda. Atop the site of the original pagoda there rises a *tahōtō*-style pagoda moved there during the Momoyama period (late 16th century).

KARUDERA Kashihara-shi, Ōkaru

This is said to have been the "clan temple" (*ujidera*) of the Karu clan. Judged from the designs on excavated tiles, it was built in the latter half of the 7th century. The Karu-no-ichi, a bustling market which had its heyday during the period when the political capital was located in the Asuka-Fujiwara region, is said to have been in the vicinity of this temple.

← *Site of Karudera seen from a distance*

KASHIWADEDERA Kashihara-shi, Kashiwade-chō

This was the *ujidera* of the Kashiwade clan. Its foundation stones are presently within in precincts of the Hōjuin. Tiles from the latter half of the 7th century have been found nearby.

← *Site of Kashiwadedera seen from a distance*

ABEDERA Historical Site Sakurai-shi, Abe

This was the *ujidera* of the Abe clan, a family which enjoyed great wealth and influence during the Asuka and Nara periods. It was built in the clan's home territory around the middle of the 7th century. Excavations have confirmed the remains of a pagoda and other buildings. The present-day Abe no Monjuin is a sort of latter-day descendant of the original temple.

← *Site of Abedera pagoda, following excavation study.*

a Tile from Karudera b Tile from Kashiwadedera c Tile from Abedera

a   b   c

(by Kakinomoto-no-Hitomaro)

By Karu road
Whose name recalls sky-flying [wild geese]
Was the village of my love
With fond attachment I yearned to visit there
Yet if I went too many times, unceasingly
People's eyes would be too many
And surely they would come to know.
So I pinned my hopes as to a great ship
Expecting that, like vines of the *sane-kazura*
Though parting, surely we should meet again
And longed for her only in secret
As in an iridescent rock-pent pool
When, as if the sun in crossing
Had gone into darkness
And the shining moon had hidden in clouds
A messenger, with catalpa wand, reported saying
That my sweetheart, who had bent to me
Like the yielding seaweed in offshore waters
Had like a colored autumn leaf
Passed on and was no more.
Hearing the sound of this sudden report
I was at a loss for what to say or do
But hearing that voice I could not stay
And hoping there might be some human feeling
To allay even the thousandth part of my longing
I left for the Karu market
That my sweetheart always came to see
But standing to listen, there wasn't heard even
The crying of birds on Unebi hill
And not a single person walked the road
Who even looked like her
So seeing nothing else to do
I only called my sweetheart's name
And waved my sleeve   *Man'yōshū 207*

To seek my love who has lost her way
In colored leaves
Too densely grown on an autumn hill
Which mountain trail to take
I do not know   *Man'yōshū 208*

OKUYAMA KUMEDERA   Asuka-mura, Okuyama

At this temple site, a large number of 7th century tiles have been unearthed, including the oldest extant *onigawara* (tiles decorating ends of roof ridges, most often sporting gargoyle or demon-face designs) which bear lotus patterns. Above the central foundation stone of the original pagoda there rises a 13-storey stone pagoda (*sekitō*) from the Kamakura period.

➡ *13-storey stone pagoda in Okuyama Kumedera*

d Tile from Kumedera   e Tile from Okuyama Kumedera

KIBI-HAIJI
Sakurai-shi, Kibi-chō

In the Kibi district of Kashihara-shi, two archaeological sites, in the neighborhoods known by the names of Daijin-yabu and Rendaiji, respectively, have produced tiles from the latter half of the 7th century. Both are called "Kibi-haiji" (meaning "abandoned temple sites in Kibi district"). One or the other is thought perhaps to have been the *ujidera* of the Kibi clan.   ⬆ *left: Rendaiji*

DAIGO-HAIJI
Kashihara-shi, Daigo-chō

In the outskirts of the Daigo district is an earth platform, in the vicinity of which have been discovered foundation stones and tiles from the latter half of the 7th century, with the result that it is thought to be a temple site. One theory links it to the "Daigoji" (written with different characters having the same pronunciation) mentioned in historical literature as having been built by Shōtoku Taishi. Certain tiles resemble tiles from the Hōryūji, a finding which is unusual with respect to architectural remains in the Asuka region.   ⬆ *right: Site of Daigo-haiji, seen from a distance*

NIKKŌJI
Kashihara-shi, Minamiura-chō

This temple is traditionally said to have been built by Shōtoku Taishi, but, judging from the tile patterns, it was more likely founded in the latter half of the 7th century.

KŌZENJI
Kashihara-shi, Kaige-chō

This temple is located at the foot of Kaguyama. In earlier times the mountain bore the alternative designation "Kōzen," and it is thought that the name of the temple, though written in different characters, may have been chosen to reflect its geographical association with the mountain. Tile remains indicate that it was probably built in the latter half of the 7th century.

WADA-HAIJI
Kashihara-shi, Wada-chō

At the site of this "abandoned temple in Wada" are the remains of an earth platform. The theory once prevailed that this was the site of the "north pagoda" mentioned in historical accounts as having been built by Soga-no-Umako on the hill known as Ōno-no-oka. However, recently the theory has gained strength that it was perhaps the site of the Kazurakidera, clan temple of the Kazuraki family. Excavations at the south side of the earth platform brought to light the remains of buildings and tiles from the first half of the 7th century.   ➡ *Ridge-end tile (shibi) unearthed at Wada-haiji*

ŌBARADERA
Historical Site   Sakurai-shi, Ōbara

From this site there remains a *fukubachi* (part of a bronze spire originally fitted to the temple's three-storey pagoda), now housed at the Danzan Jinja. From an inscription on it, we learn that the temple was built by Nakatomi-no-Ōshima in memory of Prince Kusakabe, and that it was begun in 694 (eighth year of Empress Jitō's reign) and finished in 715. Foundation stones remain on the sites of the pagoda and golden hall.

a Tile from Kibi-haiji   bc Tiles from Daigo-haiji   d Tile from Nikkōji   e Tile from Kōzenji
f Tile from Wada-haiji   g Fukubachi from Ōbaradera   h Tile from Ōbaradera

84

85

f

g

h

a Asukadera

d Toyuradera

b Asukadera

e Sakatadera

c Karudera

f Yamadadera

g Jikōji

j Kawaradera

h Moto Yakushiji

k Kidera

i Daikandaiji

l Fujiwara-no-miya

87

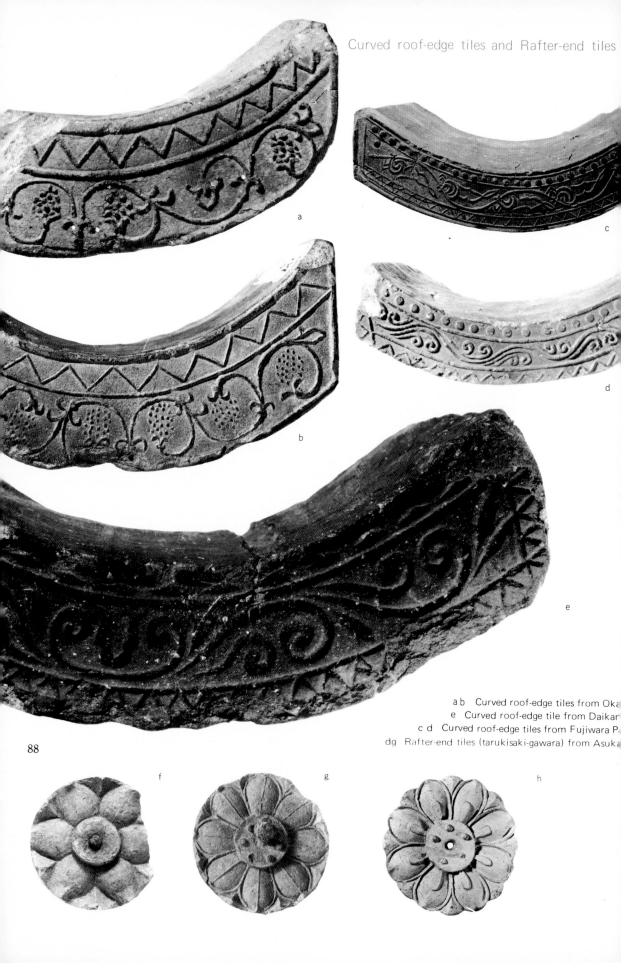

a

c

b

d

e

a b Curved roof-edge tiles from Oka
e Curved roof-edge tile from Daikan
c d Curved roof-edge tiles from Fujiwara P.
dg Rafter-end tiles (tarukisaki-gawara) from Asuka

88

f

g

h

⬆ *Onigawara from Okuyama Kumedera*

Rafter-end tile from Yamadadera
Onigawara fragment from Yamadadera
Onigawara from Okuyama Kumedera

89

ROOF TILES *(KAWARA)*

Roofs of temples and palace buildings were covered with "round roof tiles"(⌒⌒ *marugawara*, curved downward) and "curved roof tiles"(▱ *hiragawara* wider with a slight upward curve), arranged in alternate rows. Row ends were ornamented with "round roof-edge tiles" *(noki marugawara)* and "curved roof-edge tiles" *(noki hiragawara)*, both of which bore designs on their outward-facing surfaces.

Round roof-edge tiles primarily made use of lotus flower designs *(rengemon)*. The majority of such tiles from the end of the 6th century and the first half of the 7th century have simple "individual petal" (ᴗᴗ *tanben)* designs of Paekche (southwest Korean) inspiration. However, there are also some tiles of Koguryŏ (north Korean) inspiration, having vertical ridges running down the middle of each petal ᴗᴗ (see illustration "d", page 86), as well as tiles which have Silla (southeast Korean) affinities, showing animal or demon faces.

After around the middle of the 7th century, a new type of tile made its appearance. As in the case of the round roof-end tiles from the Yamadadera, there came into popularity a "layered individual petal" (ᴗ *jūben)* pattern characterized by smaller petals decoratively superimposed on the larger ones. On some tiles from this period, additional geometric designs concentrically arranged around the circumference of the lotus pattern had begun to appear. Then, during the latter part of the 7th century, from the time of the building of the Kawaradera onward, the most commonly used basic pattern, influenced by Táng Chinese tiles, came to be the "composite-petal"(ᴗᴗ *fukuben)* pattern, with the larger petals arranged in pairs, and two smaller petals superimposed on each pair. Round roofedge tiles developed elaborate design modifications such as sawtooth patterns around the outer rims.

Curved roof-edge tiles *(noki hiragawara)* first appeared during the first half of the 7th century. The curved roof-edge tiles of the Sakatadera have arabesque patterns *(karakusamon)* incised by hand. Around the middle of the 7th century, "layered arc patterns" *(Jūkomon)* were in vogue, but by the latter part of the century, arabesque patterns again comprised the mainstream of *noki hiragawara* decorative art. Temples vied with one another in devising original designs for their round and curved roof-edge tiles, seen as forming a set.

Roof of the Asukadera

The tiles which ornamented the roof of the Asukadera date from the end of the 6th century and are the oldest roof tiles known in Japan. They were made under the direction of tile craftsmen dispatched from the southwestern Korean kingdom of Paekche (Kudara). The round roof-edge tiles *(noki marugawara)*, as well as the "rafter-end tiles" *(tarukisaki-gawara)* added later in the 7th century, are identical to similar roof tiles used during the same period in Korea. Curved roof-edge tiles *(noki hiragawara)* had not yet been developed, so ordinary curved tiles *(hiragawara)* were employed, faute de mieux.

Roof of the Fujiwara Palace

Most modern-day researchers believe that roof tiles were used on palace buildings only after the end of the 7th century, beginning with the Fujiwara-no-miya. In order to cover the roofs of palace buildings, enormous quantities of tiles were needed. Production of such large quantities of tiles became possible only after the appearance of the government-operated workshops *(kōbō)* administered as a part of the *ritsuryō* governmental system which was becoming established toward the end of the 7th century. It is thought that in the case of the Fujiwara-no-miya and later palaces, only a part of the palace buildings were covered with tile, the majority being thatched with Japanese cypress bark *(hihada)*.

a Curved roof-edge tile from Sakatadera, with hand-incised arabesque pattern (karakusamon)   b Curved roof-edge tile from Okuyama Kumedera, with layered arc pattern

90

a

b

MIMINASHIYAMA

Like those waters of unsure destination
Hidden in the marshes
By the dyke of Haniyasu pond
The palace servants are in a quandary
Knowing not which way to go

Man'yōshu 201

HANIYASU

FUJIWARA-NO-MIYA

If across the Asukagawa
We had set a weir
And dammed it
Had not its flowing water
Been more calm?

Man'yōshu 197

ASUKAGAWA

Spring seems past
And summer arrived
White-bleached garments
Being dried by
Ama no Kaguyama

Man'yōshu 28

KAGUYAMA

Having nowhere to go
Like the water collected on lotus leaves
At Tsurugi pond, its name recalling a girt-on sword
With you whom I should meet as we have met before
My mother tells me not to sleep
But even so, at the bottom of that pond,
The pond that is the clear corner of my heart,
I shall not forget, until such time
As we can meet straightforwardly

Man'yōshu 3289

TSURUGI-IKE

The great sovereign [Jitō]
God that she is
Is gone to make a temporary retreat
In a hut atop the Thunder [Hill]
That recalls the clouds of heaven

Man'yōshu 235
(by Kakinomoto-no-Hitomaro)

IKAZUCHI-NO-OKA

ASUKA AND THE MAN'YŌSHŪ

From Mimoro no Kamunabiyama, clouds drawn, a rain begins to fall;
Rain merges with the mist, and besides there has blown up a wind;
He to whom my thoughts are given, he who is returning
By Magami plain, which tells of big-mouthed wolves,
Will he now be reaching home?

Man'yōshu 3268

MAGAMIHARA

ŌHARA

Having thought "*itsu shika*"
("Whenever will it be?")
A word like the *itsushiba* brush
That thrives thick-grown
At Ōhara
This night at last I am to see
The girl I love

Man'yoshu 513
(by Prince Shiki)

Alas, the Shima palace
Of our sun-prince, high and shining
From which he would have ruled the land
For a myriad generations

SHIMA

Man'yōshu 171

Poem composed by Emperor Jomei,
probably around 630, on climbing
Kaguyama

Among Yamato's clustered hills
It is close-by Ama no Kaguyama
That I climb and stand to view the land
Here and there curls of smoke rise from the plain
And gulls take wing from the lakes, endlessly
Yes, a sweet country it is
This dragonfly isle, this land of Yamato

Man'yōshū 2

ASUKA AND THE MAN'YŌSHŪ

A large number of poems having to do with Asuka are preserved in the *Man'yōshū*, Japan's earliest collection of poetry, compiled in the latter half of the 8th century. Some of the poems that have to do with Asuka were composed by such renowned poets as Kakinomoto-no-Hitomaro and Takechi-no-Kurohito, and others were composed by reigning emperors and empresses of the Asuka Period. Those poems which deal specifically with Asuka begin near the very beginning of the anthology with the poem (see above) composed by the Emperor Jomei (593~641) on the occasion of an "inspection of the country" (**kunimi**) from Ama-no-Kaguyama (one of the "Three Mountains of Yamato," now usually called simply Kaguyama) Many of the poems dealing with Asuka were composed at the time of events and incidents which are also recorded elsewhere in historical sources. Such events include military expeditions to Korea during the reign of the Empress Saimei, various moves of the dynastic residence and the building of the new capital city at Fujiwara, the civil disturbance known as the *Jinshin no ran*, the uprising of Prince Ōtsu, and the deaths of various imperial scions. These historically oriented poems, together with the other poems relating affairs of the heart or describing the natural landscape, enable us to come into contact with the consciousness and feelings of the people of that time. In the times during which the poems of the *Man'yōshū* were being written, the seminal germs of Japanese literature, seen also in the songs and poems included in the *Kojiki* and *Nihon shoki* (quasi-historical and historical records compiled in the early 8th century), were in the process of coming to flower.

⬆ *Page from Genryaku kōhon manuscript copy of part of the Man'yōshū (late 12th c.)*
◄ *Asuka region viewed from the air* ⬈ *The "Three Mountains of Yamato"*
(Yamato sanzan). Left to right: Unebiyama, Kaguyama, Miminashiyama

92

YAMATO SANZAN

"Poem of the Three Mountains" by
Naka no -Ōe (son of Jomei),
who later became Emperor Tenji

That Kaguyama vies with Miminashi
Unebi made the object of their lust
Seems thus to have been since the age of the gods
Things having been so in times long past
It is natural, perhaps, in our own fleeting world
That men contend for wives   *Man'yōshū 13*

31-syllable "answering poem" (*hanka*)

When Kaguyama and Minimashiyama
Faced each other in duel
'Twas Inamikunihara
Where [the god of Abo] came to referee   *Man'yōshū 14*

a Asukagawa (snow scene)   b Ikazuchi-no-oka

93

ASUKA

Composed by Yamabe-no-Akahito on
ascending "Kamuoka"
(most likely Ikazuchi-no-oka)

The old capital that also was our teacher
In Asuka
We had intended
To make our visits here always
Thinking it would be without end
And continue from generation to generation
Like the *tsuga* trees that grow lush
Extending their many branches
Over the Mimoro no Kamunabiyama
The old capital with its hills seen tall
And its magnificent river
The its magnificent river
The mountains especially pleasing to see
On a day in spring
The streams so especially clear
On an autumn night
Cranes winging confusedly in sunrise clouds
And frogs croaking in the evening mists
Now whenever I see the place
I cannot but weep aloud
Remembering days of old

Man'yōshū 324

Unlike the vapors that rise
From Asukagawa's every pool
This longing is not one
To be conceived perforce to pass

Man'yōshū 325

ASUKAGAWA

When spring is come
In thick profusion flowers bloom
And with the arrival of autumn
That season's colors give their cast
To vermillion spears of grain
And my heart completely yields
Like the duckweed in the rapids
Of Asuka's river that circles as a sash
Kamunabiyama whose name recalls sweet saké
If this heart must melt as the morning dew
Then so let it be
Secret mistress for whom I yearn
And would meet even openly

Man'yōshū 3266

IWARE-NO-IKE

Poem composed in 686 by Prince
Ōtsu (3rd son of Tenmu) as he wept
by the dyke of Iware pond, sentenced
to die for suspected treason

Is it today only that I will see these wild ducks crying
Echoing far along Iware pond of manifold renown
Before I must depart into hiding with the clouds

Man'yōshū 416

KAGUYAMA

Over Ama no Kaguyama
Whose name recalls the ever-enduring sky
This evening a haze is hung in shelf-like layers
How it does appear spring is upon us!

Man'yōshū 181
(Anonymou

IKAZUCHI-NO-OKA

Poem by Empress Ji
after Tenmu's dea

Autumn leaves on divine Kamu hill
That our peace-ruling king
Was wont to behold in the evening
And would visit when morning came
Would he not this very day too
Have gone to inquire of them
Would he not then tomorrow as well
Have set his eyes upon them
As I turn my gaze to discern that hill from afar
With the day's waning I am strangely sad
And when morning comes again
I while away the hours with melancholy heart
And the sleeves of my coarse-cloth robe
Have not the time to dry

Man'yōshū 15

Do they not say there even is a way
To wrap a burning flame and put it in a bag?
But what enjoyment are tricks like these
When there is no way to know his face again?

Man'yōshū 16

(Attributed to Jit

Between the blue and layered clouds
Above the northern hills
A star moves off, and so recedes the moon

Man'yōshū 16

YATSURIYAMA

Composed for Prince Niitak
(son of Tenmu, 673~73
by Kakinomoto-no-Hitomar

Our lord who rules in peace
Prince of the high-shining sun
Above the prospering palace
Snow comes and goes
Dispatched by an immemorial heaven
And like the snow
May your rounds continue
Indeed forever

Man'yōshū 26

(accompanying *tanka*

Yatsuriyama's stand of trees
Nowhere to be seen
What fun of a morning
To dash through madly falling snow

Man'yōshū 2

94

➡ *Map correlating Manyoshu poems with places in the Asuka region referred to therein.*

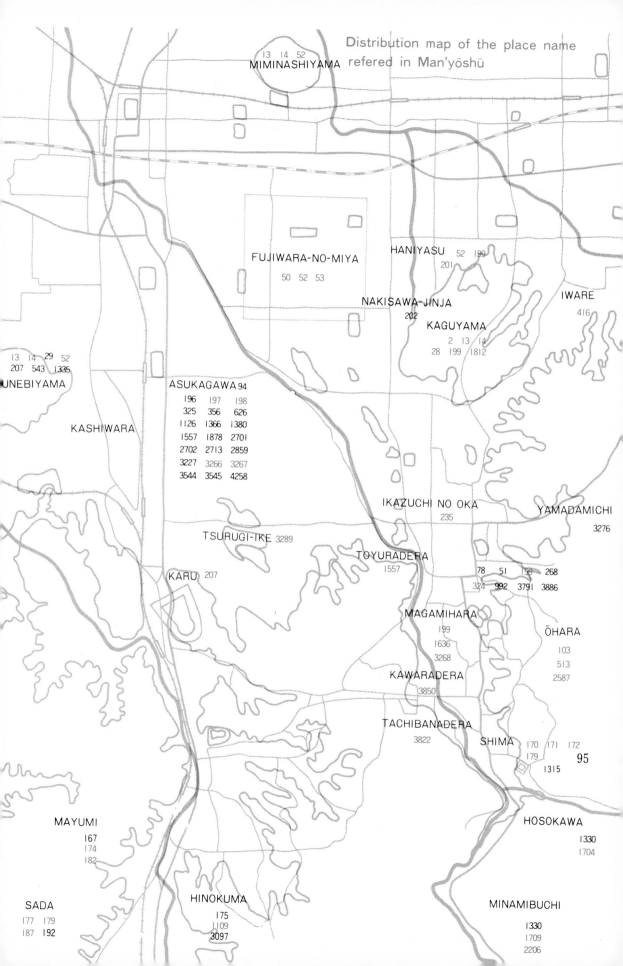

Distribution map of the place name refered in Man'yōshū

MIMINASHIYAMA
13 14 52

HANIYASU 52 199
201

FUJIWARA-NO-MIYA
50 52 53

IWARE
416

NAKISAWA-JINJA
202

KAGUYAMA
2 13 14
28 199 1812

UNEBIYAMA
13 14 29 52
207 543 1335

ASUKAGAWA 94
196   197   198
325   356   626
1126   1366   1380
1557   1878   2701
2702   2713   2859
3227   3266   3267
3544   3545   4258

KASHIWARA

IKAZUCHI NO OKA
235

YAMADAMICHI
3276

TSURUGI-IKE 3289

TOYURADERA
1557

78   51   199   268
324 992 3791 3886

KARU 207

MAGAMIHARA
199
1636
3268

ŌHARA
103
513
2587

KAWARADERA
3850

TACHIBANADERA
3822

SHIMA   170 171 172
179

95

1315

MAYUMI
167
174
182

HOSOKAWA
1330
1704

SADA
177 179
187 192

HINOKUMA
175
1109
3097

MINAMIBUCHI
1330
1709
2206

MINABUCHIYAMA

Poem presented to Prince Yuge
(6th son of Tenmu)

Here on crags at Minabuchiyama
Whose name recalls food offerings to the gods
Still unfaded fallen flakes of snow

Man'yōshū 1709

MAGAMIHARA

Snow poem by the daughter of
a place attendant

On Magami plain
Of big-mouthed wolves
Oh snow that falls
Fall not so wantonly
When there is no house for shelter

Man'yōshū 1636

ŌHARA

Composed by Emperor Tenmu
and presented to Lady Fujiwara
(one of his consorts)

At my place
A great snowfall there has been
But at your dilapidated old village at Ōhara
Later it will fall, if any

Man'yōshū 103

(The Lady's reply)

It was I who bid the Dragon God
In these hills of mine
To cause the snow to fall, whereof perchance
Some odd bits and pieces got scattered
At your place

Man'yōshū 104

In Ōhara, old and weathered
Village back home
I have left my sweetheart there
Scarcely can I sleep
But let her if she will
Appear in my dreams at least

Man'yōshū 2587

HINOKUMA

At the Sahinokuma-Hinokumagawa
If because the shoals are swift
I hold my lord's hand
What talk about us there may be!

Man'yōshū 1109

MAYUMI

Poems by servants lamenting
the death of Prince Kusakabe

Since it is Mayumi hill
Always seen before as someplace apart
Where you our lord now rest
There, alas, I keep watch
Holding it to be your eternal mansion

Man'yōshū 174

SADA

Not alas that I should have wearied
Of the Shima palace at Tachibana
Do I go to serve night watch
By the side of Sada hill

Man'yōshū 179

HOSOKAWA

Anonymous poem presented to
Prince Toneri (son of Tenmu)

Tufting, twisting
Are they not those Tamu mountain mists
So densely gathered
That make the waves in the Hosokawa rapids
Roar so loud?

Man'yōshū 1704

FUJIWARA-NO-MIYA

Poem on the well
at Fujiwara-no-miya

Our sovereign who rules in peace
Child of a high and shining sun
Gave beginning to a great palace
On the Fuji-well plain[1]
And standing on the Haniyasu embankment
She looked and saw
Green Kaguyama of Yamato
Spring hill standing luxuriant
Before the eastern gate;
Miminashi, green and pure, seen to stand
Well-proportioned, divine,
Behind the gate at the rear;
And the celebrated hills of Yoshino
Far away at the very seat of the clouds
In the direction of the front gate.
Water from this high-ruling place,
Shelter from the sky
And possessed of the heaven-knowing
Radiance of the sun
May it be everlasting
This fine clear water of the palace well.

Man'yōshū 52

(accompanying *tanka*)

How indeed one may be envious
Of those court maidens
Born successively to serve
At the great palace of Fujiwara

Man'yōshū 53

SHIMA-NO-MIYA

The birds we've set free
On the curved pond at the Shima palace
With loving attachment still they yearn
To catch his eye, and this is why their heads
They do not dip their heads beneath its surface

Man'yōshū 170

[1] The locality seems originally to have been called
Fujiigahara, or "plain of the wisteria well," later
taking the simpler name of Fujiwara, or "wisteria
plain."

CATALOGUE OF ITEMS DISPLAYED IN MUSEUM

	Item, and original location or site of excavation	Owner or donor to this exhibit	Page of photograph in this guidebook
Asuka Prehistory			
Jōmon earthenware, figurines, and stone implements	*Kashihara-shi, Kashihara*	Archaeological Museum of Nara prefecture	lab; 2i-1
Jōmon earthenware	*Asuka-mura, Oka*	Kashihara Institute of Archaeology	
Yayoi earthenware and stone implements	*Kashihara-shi, Shibu*	Nara National Cultural Properties Research Institute (NNCPRI)	1c-e; 2m-p
Large stone reaper	*Asuka-mura, Sakata*	NNCPRI	2q
Red pottery (hajiki)	*Sakurai-shi, Kami-no-ide*	NNCPRI	1gh
Gray pottery (sueki)	*Asuka-mura, Kawara*	Kawaradera	1f
Bronze arrowhead	*Kashihara-shi, Nawate-chō*	NNCPRI	2t
Iron arrowhead	*Asuka-mura, Toyura*	NNCPRI	2r
Spindle	*Asuka-mura, Toyura*	NNCPRI	2u
Curved gem (magatama)	*Asuka-mura, Toyura*	NNCPRI	2s
The Asuka Palaces			
Red and gray pottery	*Asuka-mura, Toyura*	NNCPRI	8b
Decorative brick with lotus design	*Supposed site of Oharida-no-miya*	NNCPRI	8a
Red and gray pottery	*Asuka-mura, Oka, supposed site of Asuka Itabuki-no-miya*	NNCPRI	10a
Red and gray pottery; Wooden clog and *kara-ishiki*	*Site of Asuka Kawara-no-miya*	NNCPRI	10b; 11dc
Red and gray pottery	*Asuka-mura, Asuka, supposed site of Asuka Kiyomihara-no-miya*	NNCPRI	13b
Bases of pillars	*Asuka-mura, Sakata, and site of Fujiwara-no-miya*	NNCPRI	
Red and gray pottery	*Site of Fujiwara-no-miya*	NNCPRI	16a
Roof-edge tiles	*Site of Fujiwara-no-miya*	NNCPRI	14a; 871; 88cd; 90c

a   Decorative metal fitting from coffin of Nomitani Kofun

b   Earthenware fragment with characters in charcoal ink, from site of Sakatadera

c   Pieces of reel for thread or yarn

97

a

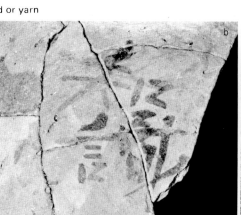
b

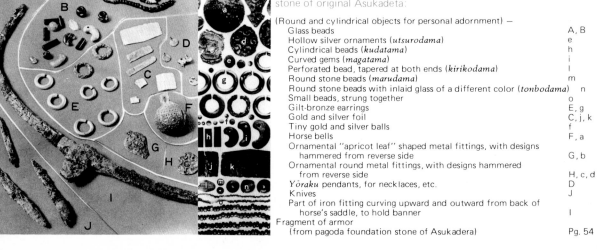

Ryokuyū hamon-sen (tiles covered with green glaze)	*Asuka-mura, Kawaradera*	NNCPRI	76b
Ryokuyū hamon-sen	*Asuka-mura, hill behind Kawaradera*	Asuka-mura Village Office	
Square Buddhist triad tile	*Asuka-mura, hill behind Kawaradera*	Asuka-mura	72
Square Buddhist triad tile	*Takatori-chō, Minami Hokkeji*	Kyoto National Museum	72b
Buddhist triad tile (tapered upper contour)	*Asuka-mura, Tachibanadera*	Tokyo National Museum	72a
Square tile with single Buddhist image	*Takatori-chō, Tsubosaka, Minami Hokkeji*	Kyoto National Museum	73c
Single Buddhist image (fragment from ornamental tile)	*Asuka-mura, Koyama, Kidera*	Kashihara Institute of Archaeology	75
Rectangular tile with seated Buddhist figures in alignment	*Sakurai-shi, site of Yamadadera*	Kyoto National Museum	73d
Face of clay figure of deity	*Asuka-mura, hill behind Kawaradera*	Asuka-mura Village Office	71
Metal ornament attached to corner rafter	*Asuka-mura, Koyama, site of Daikandaiji*	NNCPRI	65
Hanging metal ornament (wind bell)	*Asuka-mura, Koyama, site of Daikandaiji*	NNCPRI	
Earthenware fragment with characters in charcoal ink	*Asuka-mura, Sakata, site of Sakatadera*	NNCPRI	98b
Pieces of reel for thread or yarn		NNCPRI	98c

Round roof-edge tiles from Asukadera	NNCPRI	80a; 86ab	Round roof-edge tiles from Kidera	Kyoto National Museum	81d; 87k
Rafter-end tiles from Asukadera	NNCPRI	88fg	Curved roof-edge tile from Kidera		81a
Round roof-edge tiles from Sakatadera	NNCPRI	79d; 87g	Roof-edge tile from Daigandaiji	NNCPRI	
Curved roof-edge tile from Sakatadera	NNCPRI	90a	Roof-edge tiles from Moto Yakushiji	NNCPRI	64ab; 87i
Round roof-edge tile from Okuyama Kumedera	NNCPRI	83e	Round roof-edge tile from Moto Yakushiji	Kyoto National Museum	
Onigawara from Okuyama Kumedera	NNCPRI	89	Curved roof-edge tile from Okadera	Mr. Kusama Shirō, Hyogō-ken	81g
Round roof-edge tile from Toyuradera		86d	Round roof-edge tile from Ishikawa-shōja	Kyoto National Museum	99e
Round roof-edge tile from Wada-haiji	NNCPRI	85e	Round roof-edge tile from Karudera	Mr. Toyozumi Kin'ichi, Nara	99d
Round roof-edge tile from Yamadadera	NNCPRI		Round roof-edge tiles from Karudera	Kyoto National Museum	82a; 86c
Rafter-end tile from Yamadadera		88h	Round roof-edge tile from Kuriharadera	Mr. Mizuki Hazuo, Nara	80c
Roof-end tiles from Kawaradera	NNCPRI	60; 87j	Round roof-edge tile from Nikkōji	Kyoto National Museum	84d

531 Kinmei	● 538	Introduction of Buddhism from Paekche (Kudara)

531 Kinmei ● 538 Introduction of Buddhism from Paekche (Kudara)

572 Bidatsu

585 Yōmei ● 587 Soga-no-Umako defeats Mononobe-no-Moriya.

588 Sushun ● 592 Soga-no-Umako responsible for killing Emperor Sushun.

● 589 Suí unify China.

593 Suiko ● 593 Shōtoku Taishi given control over administration.

600

● 598 Suí send troops to Koguryŏ

● 600 First embassy to Suí China, sending of army to Silla.

● 603 Establishment of 12-rank official title system.

● 604 Shōtoku Taishi completes "17 Article Constitution."

● 612 Suí send troops to Koguryŏ
● 618 Táng defeat Suí.

629 Jomei ● 630 First embassy to Táng China.

642 Kōgyoku ● 643 Soga-no-Iruka kills Prince Yamashiro-no-Ōe.

645 Kōtoku ● 645 Beginning of "Taika" year period; Prince Naka-no-Ōe and Nakatomi-no-Kamatari defeat Soga-no-Emishi and Iruka.

● 646 Official rescript ordering Taika Reforms, Order for limits on size of tombs.

● 649 Prince Naka-no-Ōe accuses Soga-no-Ishikawa-maro of treason.

650

655 Saimei ● 658 Prince Arima put to death for suspected treason; Abe-no-Hirafu attacks Emishi.

661 Tenji ● 663 Japan-Paekche allied military forces defeated by Táng near mouth of present-day Kŭm River, west coast of Korea.

● 663 Táng defeats Paekche

● 668 Prince Naka-no-Ōe officially assumes throne (Emperor Tenji).

● 668 Táng defeats Koguryŏ

● 670 Household resisters are made.

672 Tenmu ● 672 Prince Ōama (Emperor Tenmu) defeats Prince Ōtomo (son of Tenji) in Jinshin Disturbance and assumes throne.

● 673 Establishment of law regulating geographical origin of officials.

● 675 Law prohibiting private ownership of servants or peasants by powerful families.

● 676 Silla unifies Korean peninsula

● 678 Law providing for evaluation of work of officials.

● 681 Decision to begin condification of ritsuryō legal system and to compile a national history.

687 Jito ● 684 Establishment of 8-grade kabane rank system for nobility and important families.

697 Monmu ● 686 First year of "Shuchō" year period; Prince Ōtsu put to death for suspected treason.

707 Genmei ● 689 Establishment of Asuka Kiyomihara-ryō legal code.

● 701 First year of "Taihō" year period; establishment of Taihō Ritsuryō legal code.

Mononobe-no-Moriya

Shōtoku Taishi

Prince Arima

57
587
62
6

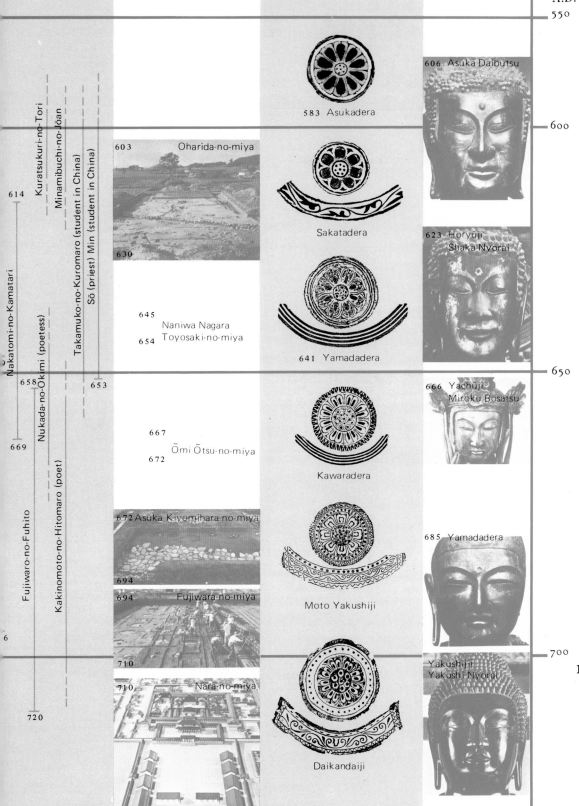

550

600

650

700

583 Asukadera

606 Asuka Daibutsu

603 Oharida-no-miya

630

Sakatadera

623 Horyuji
Shaka Nyorai

645
654 Naniwa Nagara Toyosaki-no-miya

641 Yamadadera

666 Yachuji
Miroku Bosatsu

667
672 Ōmi Ōtsu-no-miya

Kawaradera

672 Asuka Kiyomihara-no-miya

694

694 Fujiwara-no-miya

Moto Yakushiji

685 Yamadadera

710

710 Nara-no-miya

Daikandaiji

Yakushiji
Yakushi Nyorai

784

Kuratsukuri-no-Tori

Minamibuchi-no-Jōan

Takamuko-no-Kuromaro (student in China)

Sō (priest) Min (student in China)

614

Nakatomi-no-Kamatari

Nukada-no-Okimi (poetess)

658

653

669

Fujiwara-no-Fuhito

Kakinomoto-no-Hitomaro (poet)

6

720

101

Map of Historical Spots in Asuka Region

Nagaseyabu Kofun Group

Hosokawadani Kofun Group

C

Kōshinzuka Kofun

Asuka Historical Museum

Yamada

Yamadadera

Okuyama Kumedera

Yatsuri

Tate-ishi

Ōhata

Asuka-nimasu Jinja

Okadera

Sakafune-ishi

Uchiage Kofun

Ishibutai Kofun

Tate-ishi

Shimanoshō

Shima-no-miya

Sakatadera

Mara-ishi

Asuka Kiyomihara-no-miya

Ikazuchi no oka

Asuka

Miroku-ishi

Asuka Itabuki-no-miya

Okadera

Asuka Kawara-no-miya

Asuka Village Office

Miyakozuka Kofun

Sakata

Inabuchi

Ryūfukuji

Okuyama Kumedera

Ōharida-no-miya

Toyuradera

Amakashinimasu-jinja Toyura-no-miya

Asukadera

Kawaradera

Tachibanadera

Nimen-seki

Inabuchi

Tanaka-haiji

Wada-haiji

Stones with Patterned Relief Carving

Toyura

AMAGASHI NO-OKA (hill)

Kame-ishi

Tachibana

Tenmu-Jito Mausoleum

Tachibedera

Nakaoyama Kofun

Barrow Mural Museum

Kuriharadera

Kurihara

B

KASHIHARAJINGŪMAE

Umayasaka-no-miya

Ishikawashoja

Ishikawa

Tsurugi ike

SHŌBUIKE KOFUN

Oni-no-manaita

Oni-no-kawara

Asuka General Information Office

Takamatsuzuka Kofun

Takamatsuzuka Kofun

Emperor Monmu's Mausoleum

Hinokuma

Omiashi Jinja

Hinokumadera

Kashiwara Jingū

Kumedera

Umayasakadera

Karu

Karudera

Maruyama Kofun

Misa

Emperor Senka Mausoleum

Masuda-no-ike Site

Emperor Kinmei's Mausoleum

Saru-ishi

Kibi-hime O'grave

OKADERA

Numayama Kofun

Masuda-no-iwafune

Kegoshizuka Kofun

Iwayayama Kofun

Kansuzuka Kofun

Kotani Kofun

Mayumi

ASUKA

Kintetsu Ry. Yoshino Line

To Yoshino

Kintetsu Ry. Minami-Osaka Line

KASHIHARAJINGŪNISHIGUCHI

A

2

3

INDEX

Please note: designations such as "A1," "B3," etc., correspond to locations on map of historical sites in Asuka region, pages 102~3.

104

105

Acknowlegements for Photographs

Persons and institutions which kindly contributed the photographs used in this guidebook include the following:

Messrs. Aboshi Yoshinori, Akiyama Hideo, Irie Taikichi, Ishimaru Hiroshi, Kunitomo Toshitarō, Kuzunishi Sōsei, Tsuboi Ryōhei, Yazawa Yūichi; Asuka-mura Village Office, Asukaen, Benridō (publishers), Agency of Cultural Affairs, Gakushū Kenkyūsha (publishers), Iwanami Shoten (publishers), Kashihara Institute of Archaeology, Kōdansha (publishers), Kyoto National Museum, Library of Imperial Household Agency, Mainichi Shinbunsha (publishers), Nara National Museum, Committee on Education of Nara Prefecture, Archaeological Museum of Nara Prefecture, Sansaisha (publishers) and Tokyo National Museum.

Special mention must be made of the fact that the greatest part of the photographs contained in this volume were taken by Messrs. Inoue Tadao, Tsukuda Mikio and Yahata Fusō, who, together with the persons and institutions (both public and private) listed above, kindly contributed their work for this guidebook. Again we take this opportunity to express our heartfelt thanks for the suggestions and cooperation of all those persons, including those listed above, who assisted in the making of this guidebook.